VAMPIRES

To Mark Ireland

© Tom Slemen 2007

Published by The Bluecoat Press, Liverpool
Book design by March Graphic Design Studio, Liverpool
Printed by Ashford Colour Press

ISBN 978 1 904438 61 8

VAMPIRES

Tom Slemen

The Bluecoat Press

CONTENTS

Introduction

THE LATE REVEREND Christopher Neil-Smith, who died in 1995, was a High Anglican priest, who not only carried out numerous exorcisms, but was also involved to a certain extent in vampire-hunting. Authorised by the Bishop of London to tackle evil in all of its twisted forms, Reverend Neil-Smith took on many cases where people came to him with problems of a vampiric nature. Neil-Smith's definition of a vampire was that it was a half-animal, half human hybrid, and that it was usually conjured up and directed by Devil-worshippers.

In the 1970s, a woman consulted him because deep scratch-marks inexplicably appeared on her wrist each night, and she felt blood being drawn out of her body through these sinister cuts. The reverend ascertained that she had no history of self-harm or psychiatric illness, and suspected that a vampire was using her for a regular night feed. An exorcism was performed and the woman was troubled no more by the nocturnal bloodsucker. Then there was the case of the South African man who also felt his blood being sucked from his body each night, although his wounds were virtually non-existent. After the Rite of Exorcism was performed on him, the mysterious nightly siphoning off of blood ceased. The reverend also tackled a case where a man was apparently being subjected to regular vampiric attacks by his deceased brother. As the man lay in bed each night he could feel himself becoming weaker and weaker, as if something was sucking out his very life-force. The reverend performed an exorcism on him, and once again the vampire-like symptoms ceased.

Another vicar who believes in vampires, and claims to have met one of them, does not want to be named but gave me the following account. In the 1960s, he was called out to the three-storey home of a certain philanthropic Baroness in the East End of London, because of the regular appearance of a cloaked stranger who had appeared out of nowhere in several of the bedrooms and seduced three women by biting their necks and breasts. The reverend confronted what he believed was a vampire and burned its face with holy water. After thrusting a crucifix in the face of the night visitor, it turned abruptly and hurled itself through a window, crashing to the pavement two storeys below without sustaining any harm. The Baroness said she had been haunted by the very same entity as a teenager, whenever she had stayed at her uncle's home on the island of St Michael's Mount. The reverend described the vampire to me as a caped man with curly white hair (resembling a periwig), and years later he came across an eighteenth century engraving in a book, of a man who looked remarkably like the vampire. That engraving was of a mysterious historical personage known as the Count of St Germain. Historians have a difficult time explaining the Count, because of his incredible lifespan. Some called him the 'Undying Count', and the great writer and philosopher Voltaire described him as, "A man who does not die and knows everything". Here is the Count's strange history:

In 1745, one of the most intriguing people in history visited London; a man who was said to be over a thousand years old. Some said he was in league with the Devil, others thought he was a Himalayan yogi of the highest order; all that is certain is that, according to written historical references, a Count St Germain was on the European scene from 1651 to 1896 – a period of two hundred and forty-five years! Unable to explain the incredible lifespan of this man, historians either omitted him from the history books altogether, or simply claimed that several impostors, in different time periods, were responsible for perpetuating the myth. However, if we face the unadulterated facts about the Count as they were written down, they paint a complex and deeply perplexing picture.

When the English soldiers returned from the Holy Land after the third Crusade came to a disastrous end in the twelfth century, they brought back with them many fabulous tales of the mysterious Orient. One particular story was of a man known in the East as the 'Wandering Jew'. The story went as follows: In the Judgement Hall of Pontius Pilate, there was a Jewish doorkeeper named Cartaphilus, who was actually present at the trial of Jesus of Nazareth. When Jesus was dragging his cross through the streets on the way to Calvary, he halted for a moment to rest, and Cartaphilus stepped out from the large crowd lining the route and told Him to hurry up. Jesus looked at Cartaphilus and said, "I will go now, but thou shall wait until I return." The Roman soldiers escorting Jesus to the crucifixion site pushed Cartaphilus back into the crowd, and Jesus continued on his way. What did Jesus mean? Many years later, the doorkeeper gradually realised that all his friends were dying of old age, whilst he had not aged at all. He remembered Jesus's words and shuddered, as it dawned on him that he would have to wander the earth without ageing until Christ's Second Coming.

This tale was dismissed by the religious authorities of the day as an apocryphal yarn, and the legend of the Wandering Jew was later interpreted by the Christians as an allegorical story, symbolizing the global wanderings and persecutions of the Jewish race because of their refusal to accept Jesus as the long-awaited Messiah. The tale gradually passed into European folklore and joined the other fairy tales of the Middle Ages.

Then, in the thirteenth century, a number of travellers returning to England from the Continent spoke of meeting and hearing of a strange and blasphemous man who claimed to have been around when Christ was on earth. These curious reports were later strengthened in 1228 when an Armenian Archbishop visited St Albans. He told his astonished audience that he had recently dined with an unusual man who had confessed to being Cartaphilus, the man who had mocked Christ. Many more encounters with Cartaphilus were reported in the following centuries, each successive meeting seeming to take place closer and closer to Western Europe.

Then one day, in the year 1740, a mysterious man, clad in black, arrived in Paris. The gaudily-dressed fashion-conscious Parisians instantly noticed the sinister stranger, and admired the dazzling array of diamond rings which adorned each of his fingers. The man in black also wore diamond-encrusted shoe-buckles, an ostentatious display of wealth suggestive of his being an aristocrat, yet nobody in Paris could identify him. From the Jewish cast of his handsome countenance, some of the superstitious Parisians believed he was Cartaphilus, the Wandering Jew.

The man of mystery later identified himself as the Count of St Germain, and he was quickly welcomed into the fashionable circles of Parisian life. In the distinguished company of writers, philosophers, scientists, freemasons and aristocrats, the Count displayed a veritable plethora of talents. He was an accomplished pianist, a gifted singer and violinist, a linguist who spoke fluent Spanish, Greek, Italian, Russian, Portugese, Chinese, Arabic, Sanskrit, English and, of course, French. The Count of St Germain was also a fine artist, an historian, and a brilliant alchemist. He maintained that he had travelled widely, and recounted his many visits to the court of the Shah of Persia, where he had studied the closely-guarded science of improving and enlarging gemstones. The Count also hinted that he had learned many other arcane lessons of the occult.

What stunned his awestruck listeners most was his insinuation that he was over a thousand years old, which came about one evening when the conversation turned to religious matters. When the Count was invited to comment on the subject, he movingly described Christ as if he had personally known him, and talked in detail about the miraculous water-into-wine miracle at the marriage feast of Cana, as if he were describing a party-trick. After his peculiar anecdote, the Count suddenly became tearful, and in a broken, uncharacteristically sombre voice, declared, "I had always known that Christ would meet a bad end."

The Count of St Germain also spoke of other historical celebrities, such as Cleopatra and Henry VIII, as if he had known them personally. Whenever sceptical historians would try to trip him up by questioning him about trivial historical details that were not widely known, the Count would always reply with astonishing accuracy, leaving the questioner thoroughly perplexed.

The Count's claim to be much older than he looked was reinforced one day when the old Countess von Georgy met him. She immediately recognized the enigmatic nobleman as the same individual she had met fifty years previously in Venice, where she had been the ambassadress. She was amazed that the Count still looked the same age as he was then, about forty-five. She was naturally confused, and asked him if his father had been in Venice at that time. The Count shook his head and assured her that it had been himself, and he further baffled her by telling her how beautiful she had looked as a young woman and how he had enjoyed playing her favourite musical piece on the violin. The Countess recoiled in disbelief and said, "Why, you must be almost one hundred years old."

"That is not impossible," replied the Count, enigmatically.

"You are a most extraordinary man ..." she exclaimed, " ... a devil!"

This touched a raw nerve, and in a raised voice, he replied, "For pity's sake! No such names!" and turned his back on the shocked Countess and indignantly stormed out of the room.

The King of France, Louis XV was intrigued by the stories of the mysterious Count St Germain and sought him out and offered him an invitation to attend the royal court. The Count accepted the invitation, and succeeded in captivating the king and his courtiers, as well as Madame de Pompadour, the king's mistress. During the spectacular banquets that were held at court, the Count would abstain from all food and wine, occasionally sipping mineral water. When he did dine, it was always in private, and precisely what he did consume is not known, although some of the courtiers claimed he was a vegetarian.

Count St Germain arrived in London in 1743 and lodged at a house in St Martin's Street. He stayed in the capital for two years, and during that time he set up a laboratory and carried out mysterious experiments, which appeared to have been of an alchemical nature. His work was closely guarded, but seemingly involved attempts at manufacturing artificial diamonds. During his stay in London, the Count was a frequent guest at the prestigious Kit-Kat club, where he mingled with members of the highest nobility. It was here that he once astounded members by referring to two inventions on which he was working: the steam train and the steamboat. This was twenty years before James Watt put together his crude prototype of the steam engine, and eighty-four years before George Stephenson's Rocket steam train of 1829.

In 1745, the year of the Jacobite Rebellion in Britain, the Count St Germain was arrested at a coffee house in Paternoster Row and charged with spying. Horace Walpole, the son of Sir Robert Walpole, Britain's first Prime Minister, mentioned the incident in a letter to his lifelong correspondent, Sir Horace Mann:

The other day they seized an odd man who goes by the name the name of the Count St Germain. He has been here these two years, and will not tell who he is, or whence he came, but professes that he does not go by his right name. He sings and plays on the violin wonderfully, is mad and not very sensible.

At a time when English xenophobia was at an all-time high because many foreigners, especially Frenchmen were known to be sympathetic to the Jacobite cause, the Count should have been imprisoned. But instead, he was released. Just why this occurred is still a mystery. One curious report circulating at the time claimed that he used hypnotic suggestion to persuade his detainers of his innocence. This is a real possibility, because, true enough, Anton Mesmer, who is credited with the discovery of hypnotism, stated years before that the Count possessed a 'vast understanding of the workings of the human mind' and had been directly responsible for teaching him the art of hypnosis.

In 1756, the Count was spotted by Sir Robert Clive in India, and in 1760, history records that King Louis XV sent Monsieur St Germain to The Hague to help settle the peace treaty between Prussia and Austria. In 1762, he took part in the deposition of Peter III of Russia and took an active role in bringing Catherine the Great to the throne.

The enigmatic Count opened a mass-production factory in Venice in 1769, where he developed a synthetic form of silk. During this period he also executed several magnificent sculptures in the tradition of classical Greece. A year later he was again active, this time interfering in the politics of other nations. He was even seen in the uniform of a Russian General with Prince Alexei Orloff in Leghorn!

After the death of Louis XV in 1774, the man from nowhere turned up unexpectedly in Paris and warned the new monarch, King Louis XVI and his Queen, Marie Antoinette, of the approaching danger of the French Revolution, which he described as a 'gigantic conspiracy' that would overthrow the order of things. Of course, the warning went unheeded, and among the final entries in her diary, Marie Antoinette recorded her regret at not taking the Count's advice.

In February 1784, Prince Charles of Hesse-Cassel, Germany, announced the news that the Count was dead, and was to be buried at the local church in Eckenforde. Among the crowds that attended the funeral service were many prominent occultists, including Count Cagliostro, Anton Mesmer, and the philosopher Louis St Martin. The coffin was lowered into the grave, and many of the mourners sobbed at what seemed so unbelievable – the death of the immortal Count. But that is not the end of the story, for a year later, in 1785, a congress of

Freemasons was held in Paris. Among the Rosicrucians, Kabbalists and Illuminati, was the supposedly dead Count St Germain!

Thirty-six years after his funeral, the Count was seen by scores of people in Paris. These included the diarist Mademoiselle d'Adhemar, and the educationalist Madame de Genlis and both women said the Count still looked like a sprightly forty-five year-old.

In 1870, the Emperor Napoleon III was so fascinated by the reports of 'The Undying Count' that he ordered a special commission to be set up at the Hotel de Ville to investigate the nobleman. But the findings of the commission never came to a conclusion, because in 1871, a mysterious fire of unknown origin gutted the Hotel de Ville, destroying every document related to the self-styled Count.

The Count St Germain was briefly seen in Milan in 1877, attending a meeting of the Grand Lodge of Freemasons and in 1896, the theosophist Annie Besant said she had met the Count, and around the same year, Russian theosophist Madame Blavatsky also said that he had been in contact with her, and she proclaimed that he belonged to a race of immortals who lived in a subterranean country called Shambhala, north of the Himalayas. In 1897, the French singer Emma Calve also claimed that the Count St Germain had paid her a visit, and she called him a 'great chiromancer' who had told her many important truths.

The story of the immortal Count went out of vogue at the beginning of the twentieth century – until August 1914, that is, in the early days of the First World War. Two Bavarian soldiers captured a Frenchman of Jewish appearance in Alsace and during the all-night interrogation, the prisoner-of-war stubbornly refused to give his name. Then, suddenly, in the early hours of the morning, the unidentified Frenchman became very irritable and started ranting about the futility of the war. He told his captors, "Throw down your guns!" he told his captors. "The war will end in 1918 with defeat for the German nation and her allies!" One of the soldiers, Andreas Rill, laughed at the prisoner's words. He thought the man was merely expressing the hopes of every Frenchman, but he was intrigued by the prisoner's other prophecies ...

"Everyone will be a millionaire after the war! There will be so much money in circulation, people will throw it from windows and no one will bother to pick it up. You will need to carry it around in wheelbarrows to buy a loaf!" said the Frenchman, predicting the rampant inflation of post-war Germany. The soldiers scoffed at his words but allowed him to ramble on. He gave them more future-history lessons: "After the confetti money will come the Antichrist. A tyrant from the lower classes wearing an ancient symbol. He will lead Germany into another global war in 1939, but will be defeated six years on, after doing inhuman, unspeakable things." At this point the Frenchman became incoherent; he started to sing, then began to sob. Thinking he was mad, the soldiers decided to let him go, and he disappeared back into obscurity. His identity is still unknown. Could he have been Count St Germain?

Today, most historians regard Count St Germain as nothing more than a silver-tongued charlatan. But there are so many unanswered questions. What was the source of the Count's wealth, for example? How can we possibly explain his longevity? For that matter, where did he come from? If he had been an impostor, surely someone would have recognized him.

The only surviving manuscript written by the Count, entitled, 'La Tres Sainte Trinosophie', is in the library at Troyes, France, and to date, it has resisted every attempt to be fully deciphered, but one decoded section of the text states:

We moved through space at a speed that can only be compared with nothing but itself. Within a fraction of a second the plains below us were out of sight and the Earth had become a faint nebula.

What does this signify? Could it be that the Count St Germain was some type of traveller in the realms of space and time? A renegade timelord from the future who liked to meddle with history? If this were so, perhaps he really had spoken with Christ and the kings of bygone days. Was the Count a type of vampire? I personally don't believe he was, but he does exemplify the possibility of beings on this earth with incredible life-spans. Who knows if there are evil beings at large in the world today who have been around for centuries?

This brings me back to the entity that troubled the household in Camden, London, in the 1960s. With holy water, a crucifix, and most importantly, his faith, the young priest confronted a spine-chilling man in a white periwig and a long flowing white cloak who materialised almost every night in the home of the Baroness who did charity work for the poor of East London. The attacks always happened after midnight, and the vampiric entity would be heard creeping down the stairs from the attic. The first casualty was seventeen-year-old Claudia who had been rescued from the streets of London by the Baroness after running away from her violent father in Nottingham. Claudia was awakened at around 12.40am by what she initially believed to be kisses to her neck. She found an oddly-dressed stranger leaning over her, gently biting her neck. She screamed and the stranger clamped a cold hand over her mouth and gazed into her eyes. Claudia felt lethargic and all fear left her. The man bit her neck again and sucked the blood from her for an interminable time, before Claudia drifted into a strange dreamless sleep.

The same thing happened to fifty-year-old Bridget, staying at the same house. She managed to close her eyes, so the vampire's hypnotic gaze could not silence her. The stranger muttered something in a foreign tongue and stormed out of the room. Bridget awoke one morning with a deep cut to the left of her throat that wouldn't stop bleeding for almost an hour. Three nights later a woman in her thirties who cooked at the house woke up just after midnight to the sensation of someone biting into her breast. "Jesus protect me!" she cried, and felt the thing rise off her in the darkness, followed by the heavy slamming of the bedroom door.

Then one morning, at 4am, the vampire appeared in the Baroness's room. She bravely asked him what he wanted, and after standing at her bedside for a minute in silence, he suddenly smiled, then left. The priest who was called in to deal with this unusual persecutor, held a vigil at the house each night for a week – before the cloaked menace put in an appearance in Claudia's room. The girl threw a Bible at the unearthly visitor and he fled on to the landing and down the stairs. The priest had been patrolling the landings and saw the shadowy figure in the white periwig hurrying towards him. He produced a crucifix and held it out at the weird intruder, who juddered to a halt. By the feeble light of a lamppost shining into the house, the clergyman could see that the vampire was a swarthy long-nosed man with intense dark eyes. He was staring at the small silver crucifix in abject fear. The priest took out a small bottle of holy water, lifted it to his mouth, and removed the cork with his teeth. The vampire backed away, sensing what was to come. The holy water was hurled at the black figure, who shrieked and threw himself through the window, crashing through wood and glass and landing in the street below – apparently without harm – for he picked himself up and ran off into the wet and gloomy night. The priest bravely tried to pursue the bloodsucker but the vampire was far too agile; at one point bounding over an eight-foot-tall wall. He never returned to the home of the Baroness, and his identity remains a mystery, although the priest, who later saw an engraving of the so-called immortal Count of St Germain, believed he was the vampire he had tackled that rainy night in the 1960s.

Vampires are still being reported to this day. Google 'Birmingham Vampire' to see what I mean – or enter 'Chupacabra' into a search engine and you will find copious internet reports of a creature that sucks animals' blood, yet remains invisible. Many people refuse to believe in ghosts until they encounter one, but knowing what I know about the vampire, I hope you, the reader, will never encounter one, unless of course, you wish to become one yourself one day …

… Sleep well!

VAMPIRES OF THE LIFE FORCE

WHEN I WAS A CHILD, adults confidently used to reassure me that vampires such as the legendary Dracula did not, and never had, existed. Today, I know that they were wrong to dismiss the bloodsuckers so readily. Believe me, vampires certainly do exist, although many incidents attributed to vampires turn out to be fake but a surprising number are all too genuine.

Firstly, one must look at the cults that can be found in several major cities (most notably San Francisco and London), in which members not only drink each other's blood, but also that of sacrificed people and animals. Not only are such practices thoroughly repellant to most people, they are also highly dangerous in the AIDS era.

Nevertheless, a cursory browse of the Internet will come up with a large number of these vampiric sects. This drinking of blood is usually indulged in for erotic reasons, but throughout history, from the days of the ancient Egyptians to the present day, there have been many well-documented reports of real vampires attacking and subduing their victims. Nor do we have to go back thousands of years to find such reports. There have been several vampire alerts in modern times, and they are still occurring today.

Vampire at Large

On 16 April 1922, a man was admitted to London's Charing Cross Hospital bleeding from a strange deep wound in his neck. Pale from blood loss, the man was very vague when the medical staff questioned him about the circumstances surrounding his injury. Just before he passed out, he told them that all he could remember was that he had been turning a corner off Coventry Street, when he felt an agonising stabbing sensation in his neck. As he had not seen his attacker, he was unable to give the police anything to go on.

A few hours later, another man was brought into the same hospital with an almost identical wound to his neck. He too had felt a sharp pain in his neck before losing consciousness and the attack had taken place at the very same turning off Coventry Street near Piccadilly Circus. This second victim was equally at a loss to explain the circumstances of his attack. He told the staff that, as far as he was aware, there had been no one within at least twenty feet of him when it happened and so he could not provide a description of his assailant.

Incredibly, a third patient was later taken to Charing Cross Hospital, and he too had a deep wound to his neck – which he had received at the same corner in Coventry Street where the previous two incidents had occurred. The *People* newspaper covered the strange story, and rumours of a vampire at large in the West End spread like wildfire. Alas, the invisible Coventry Street attacker was never apprehended by Scotland Yard, but the case has all the hallmarks of a true vampire assault.

ME? Or Something More Sinister?

Contrary to popular belief, not all vampires are shape-shifters who turn into bats and fly off in search of their victims, although the dark talent of such metamorphosis was described by Bram Stoker in his 1897 novel *Dracula*. From the data we have on actual vampire attacks, it would seem that many of these strange bloodthirsty beings have the ability to 'teleport' themselves about, either in physical form, or by somehow projecting their 'wraith', or astral body, to the victim's home. Furthermore, there seems to be a species of vampire that rarely bites his or her victims in order to imbibe their blood. Instead, this type of vampire prefers to draw off the very life-energy of the victims, leaving them physically and mentally exhausted and feeling quite ill.

In fact, the symptoms of this subtle form of vampire assault are identical to a strange condition that is now becoming increasingly prevalent in the civilised world – ME – short for myalgic encephalomyelitis. This is a benign but debilitating (and often long-lasting) condition which allegedly occurs out of the blue, and causes headaches, weakness, muscular pain, extreme fatigue and even fever. Over 150,000 people in Britain are affected and for some reason, most of the sufferers are women. The condition is highly controversial and the medical authorities still cannot agree amongst themselves about the true nature of ME, or indeed, if it actually exists at all. Some doctors think the condition is purely psychosomatic (originating in the mind), while others believe it has a link to the coxsackieviruses in the human body. Whatever the cause, this strange incapacitating condition is reaching pandemic proportions all over the world.

'Love Bites'

No one had even heard of ME in 1970, but in the summer of that year, Judith, a nineteen-year-old girl from Winsford, Cheshire, was suddenly stricken with ME-like symptoms. A doctor examined her and initially diagnosed flu, but the girl returned a week later, accompanied by her mother, complaining that she felt worse rather than better. She was very pale and lethargic, and had a number of unusual purple marks on her neck and breasts. The doctor took the discolourations to be 'love bites' and this time concluded that she was suffering from a form of glandular fever that is quite common amongst teenagers and is often caught from kissing. Judith's mother was not convinced and told the doctor about her daughter's screaming fits in the dead of night and the strange lucid nightmares that haunted her sleep.

Judith's accounts of these night terrors resulted in her being referred to Dr Michael Dwerringwood, a psychiatrist. During her sessions with Dwerringwood, she was coaxed into revealing the exact form that these night terrors took. Her face was creased with anxiety as she described how she now dreaded going to bed, because each night she felt a sinister cold presence invading her bedroom around midnight. As she lay quaking beneath the covers, filled with horrible anticipation of what was to come, a young man in black would suddenly appear at the foot of her bed, leering at her in the most disgusting and suggestive way.

"Does this man look like anyone you know?" asked Dwerringwood, who could clearly see how upset she was. "Do you recognise him at all?"

"Yes … yes I do. He looks like someone who lives near us. His name's Lazzlo and he's an art student, I think."

"And this Lazzlo chap, is there anything odd or unusual about him when you see him in the daytime?"

"Well no, he's sort of foreign looking and I suppose some people might think he's attractive, because he is quite good-looking but he gives me the creeps. There's something eerie about him."

She then went into detail about the first assault in her bedroom.

"I was just nodding off to sleep, when I felt a cold hand stroking my breasts. I opened my eyes but could see nothing because the room was in darkness. Someone was on top of me in the bed, and he was kissing me and biting my neck, and I was so frightened I couldn't move or cry out. I closed my eyes and hoped I was just having a nightmare, but when I opened them he was still there. From the light of the lamppost shining into my bedroom I saw his face. It was Lazzlo."

Yet Judith somehow knew that her attacker – despite looking and feeling all too real – was actually some kind of paranormal entity, because when she screamed, he disappeared as quickly as he had come, even though the window and door remained closed. He seemed to have the ability to materialise and dematerialise at will, literally vanishing into thin air.

The young man, whom she identified as Lazzlo Ordog, was a twenty-three-year-old Hungarian art student. He cut quite an imposing figure, being over six-foot-four in height with olive skin, black slicked-back hair and a lively pair of dark brown probing eyes, which she said seemed to be able to penetrate into the very depths of her soul.

Despite being able to give such a good description of Lazzlo, Dr Dwerringwood's suspicions lay elsewhere and he gently began questioning Judith about her relationship with her father, as he secretly suspected him of being the nocturnal culprit. There had been no sign of any break-in at the house, so Judith's story didn't stack up.

"What do you mean? My dad died a few years ago," said Judith, her lip beginning to tremble.

"Oh! I'm sorry to hear that. Here you are, dear," said the psychiatrist, handing her the box of tissues that he always kept to hand for occasions such as these. "Well, let me see … do you have any uncles, or other male relatives living at your house?"

"What are you trying to say, doctor? No, I don't as a matter of fact, unless you count our Graham, my six-year-old brother. Is he under suspicion as well?" she sniffed.

"Now, Judith, there's no need to get upset. I'm only trying to get to the bottom of all this so that I can help you."

"Yes, I know you are, doctor. I'm sorry, but you don't seem to be listening to me when I say that he's so real … yet he's not real … he can't be … real people don't just appear and disappear like that, do they?"

Judith left each session feeling emotionally drained and increasingly helpless and frustrated. She couldn't blame Dr Dwerringwood for barking up the wrong tree. He was out of his depth but it wasn't his fault. How could she begin to explain to him something that she didn't even understand herself.

Then came the bizarre twist in this intriguing case. A second girl in Judith's neighbourhood was referred to the same psychiatrist. Zara had just turned sixteen, and on examination her body displayed the same cluster of love-bites on her neck and breasts. She also exhibited the same apathetic symptoms as Judith, and stranger still, this girl also tremblingly related how a 'ghost' had got into bed with her on some nights and tried to have sex with her. Dwerringwood asked Zara to describe this ghost, and the girl's descriptions matched Judith's in every detail. The apparition was of a handsome but spooky young man with black hair and penetrating eyes. As with Judith, it was the eyes which she found particularly unnerving.

Probing further, Dwerringwood gently suggested that perhaps Zara had just been having a bad dream, a nightmare, which had been unusually realistic. But no, she insisted that she had been wide awake throughout each of the ghastly nightly ordeals which stretched back over several months. The psychiatrist then asked her if she knew of any person who resembled her attacker, and she said yes, she did know of such a person. She didn't know his name, but she knew the street where he lived – the very same street where Lazzlo Ordog was residing!

The police were powerless to quiz the Hungarian on the strength of such bizarre testimonies from the two teenaged girls, but

Dwerringwood had heard those harrowing testimonies at first hand and had seen the fear on the girls' faces. He therefore decided to break with protocol and pay a visit to Lazzlo himself.

The landlady who ran the small boarding house admitted the psychiatrist into the cramped hall and called down Mr Ordog, telling him that he had a visitor. Somewhere at the top of the dark house a door creaked open and the tall wiry student silently descended the stairs looking furtively at Dwerringwood with a half-smile on his lips and giving the disquieting impression that he had been expecting him to call. The psychiatrist introduced himself and asked if he could speak to him in private for a few minutes. Ordog simply nodded and beckoned him to follow him up to his quarters in the attic of the old lodging house, which he was evidently using as his studio, as several canvases were propped up on easels and half empty tubes of paint and brushes were scattered about on every surface. All of his paintings were of female nudes, and most were incomplete, but Dwerringwood's eyes were immediately drawn to two finished watercolours lying side by side in the corner of the room. The subjects of these paintings bore an uncanny resemblance to Dwerringwood's two young patients, Judith and Zara.

Looking him straight in the eye, the doctor confronted the artist, and asked for the names of the models who had posed for the two paintings. The question had an immediate effect, wiping the sly smile off Lazzlo's face and putting him on the defensive.

"I no use the model. I am painting them from ze imagination," he cried, his dark eyes flashing with rage, as if his artistic integrity had just been called into question.

Years of listening to patients on his couch had made Dr Dwerringwood skilled in reading people's body language, facial expressions and emotional reactions and he instantly recognised Ordog's behaviour as being that of a guilty man. He decided to get straight to the point. "I'll tell you what I think, Mr Ordog. I think you are the menace who is haunting the dreams of two of my young patients. More specifically, those two girls young girls over there!" and he pointed to the two pictures lying side by side over in the corner of the studio. "For your information, both girls have identified you as the sexual predator who is making their lives a misery and I'd like to hear your theory as to why that should be the case."

The Hungarian couldn't maintain eye-contact with the psychiatrist, shrugging his shoulders in response to Dwerringwood's accusations and pretending to busy himself with the arrangement of his tubes of paint. Then he suddenly spun round and declared with ill-concealed irritation, "Girls are crazy! Zey are mad! Why you listen to zem?"

Dr Dwerringwood shrank back from those dark staring eyes and at last understood something of how the girls must have felt. He too now felt uneasy about being alone with this weird art student and decided to leave without further ado.

As he reached the door, Lazzlo grabbed his shoulder, saying, "What are you zinking of zese silly girls' stories? Are you believing zem?"

Dwerringwood felt the hairs stand up on the back of his neck. "I don't know," he muttered, without looking back, then virtually ran down the stairs two at a time. The encounter had left him deeply shaken.

When the psychiatrist returned home, he found his pet cat lying dead on his doorstep. There were no signs of physical injury on the cat's body, so he took it to the vet, who was a friend of his. The vet could not establish a reason for the cat's death, but Dwerringwood was convinced that it was in some way connected to his meeting with the sinister Hungarian painter.

On the following night, as Dwerringwood was watching the late news on television, the mirror above his fireplace suddenly split in half with a loud crack. No matter how hard he tried to convince himself that there was a rational explanation for the cracked mirror, he could not, and later that same night, when he retired to bed, he caught a glimpse of a man's silhouette standing at the top of his stairs. The shadow-like figure vanished a split-second after he had glanced at it, but he was pretty sure that it was Lazzlo Ordog's distinctive outline. The psychiatrist knew he had not imagined the figure, even though its transient appearance flew in the face of reason, like everything else connected with this baffling case.

Respecting his patients' confidentiality, Dwerringwood had never told his fiancée Glynis about the succession of strange incidents, or about the mysterious Hungarian, but one night she was lying in bed with him when she woke up choking. She felt a pair of powerful ice-cold hands wrapped around her throat, throttling the life out of her. As soon as she managed to let out a stifled scream, the strangling sensation instantly ceased. She was so certain that there was an attacker in the bedroom, that she jumped out of bed and rushed to switch on the light, but there was nobody there – the room was just as it should have been.

Dwerringwood racked his brains trying to make sense of all these strange goings on, and wondered what exactly he was up against. He was a man of science, of rationality, and he felt completely out of his depth tackling the menacing Lazzlo Ordog.

One afternoon he was drinking a cup of tea in a break between patients, when a bizarre thought dawned on him: what if the Hungarian was some sort of vampire? It was a far-fetched idea, but the more he thought about the Hungarian, the more everything seemed to stack up and the less ludicrous his theory seemed. So he decided to act on his hunch. He obtained two copies of the Bible and went out and bought three small crucifixes. He left one of the Bibles in Judith's bedroom and the other in Zara's. He also gave each of them a crucifix, advising them to wear it at all times, but especially when they went to bed.

Scarcely believing what he was doing, Dwerringwood hung the third crucifix from a chain about his own neck. That night when he went to bed, he turned off the lamp and settled down to sleep. He was just nodding off when a low gruff voice, seething with hatred, whispered in his ear, "I'll break your neck one day". The voice sounded as if it had come from someone standing at his bedside, yet there was no one there.

Judith and Zara did as they were bid and wore the crucifixes and left the Bibles in their rooms at all times. They were soon enjoying a quiet and untroubled night's sleep. They also regained their zest for living, their overall health improved, and the purple contusions quickly faded from their bodies.

Some time later, Dwerringwood called at the lodging house to question Lazzlo once more. This time, the psychiatrist carried a Bible and was wearing his crucifix, ready to confront the creepy young man and so get to the bottom of the mystery, but Lazzlo had left. The landlady said that he had moved out during the night without leaving her a forwarding address. Dwerringwood's instinct to use the Bibles and the crucifixes seemed to have paid off because there were no more strange happenings in his household, or that of his two young patients. Yet for many years afterwards, he tried to rationalise the whole vampire episode, and wondered if he had simply been caught up in a case of hysteria, autosuggestion and coincidence.

Curiously, in October 1991, there was a haunting reported in Winsford. In the very house where the teenager Judith had lived in the 1970s. A young woman awoke one morning at four o'clock and saw a man in black, with his arms outstretched, floating close to the ceiling directly above her bed. Terrified by the levitating phantom, she hid under the bedcovers, quaking with fear. When she finally summoned up enough courage to take another peek at the ceiling, she saw that the black-clad figure had vanished. Is it possible that the hovering entity was Lazzlo Ordog, out on the prowl again?

According to the acupuncturists of ancient China, the health of a person depended on the life-force – ch'i. If ch'i did not flow smoothly and harmoniously throughout the body, then physical and mental sickness were said to result. Ch'i was regarded as the very essence of the human soul, and was said to circulate in the body under the skin through a series of specific channels known as meridians.

Recent scientific research has proved beyond doubt that the human body is buzzing with electric fields, and furthermore, any interference with these fields can have serious repercussions for the state of a person's health. It has been proven for example, that children living in close proximity to electric pylons and electrical substations are at an increased risk of developing leukaemia, because strong electromagnetic fields have a detrimental effect on the human body's immune system. Perhaps this is how Lazzlo and others of his kind prey on their victims; by sapping the very essence of their life-energy, or ch'i, as both the Chinese and Western acupuncturists call it. For all we know, the parasitic vampires may be at large at this very moment in our society, draining the energy of their unsuspecting victims. Could this explain the explosion in recent years of ME cases?

24

Drained

Another case of a psychic vampire attack allegedly took place in Swindon in the 1980s.

In the summer of 1981, twenty-five-year-old Sarah went to live in Deacon Street, Swindon, to look after her seventy-five-year-old Aunt Esther, who was recovering from a mild stroke. One humid summer night, at around 11.45pm, she had retired to bed but had found difficulty sleeping. The air was thick and clammy, so she threw back the bedcovers and opened the window as wide as it would go. A full moon was hanging just above the horizon, its pale edges blurred by the dense murky atmosphere.

Sarah returned to bed and settled down to try and get some sleep on top of the duvet and was finally just drifting off to sleep when she suddenly had the eerie feeling that she was being watched, which jolted her awake. Fully alert, she sat up and glanced towards the open window from where a large dark shape flitted away. It couldn't have been a bat because it was far too big and there was no question of it being an optical illusion, because it had momentarily blocked out the moonlight pouring into the room and had cast a shadow that flitted across the bed, which begged the question, what exactly was it?

Hurriedly slamming shut the window, Sarah lay back on the bed, wide awake and wondering what the shape could have been. She was now even more restless and could not settle down to sleep. At ten minutes past midnight she turned over so that she was facing the bedroom door – and saw something which was to haunt her for the rest of her life. Creeping silently underneath the door, came an even more ominous dark shape, which slid like a black liquid through the centimetre-high gap until it began to form into a flat, two-dimensional, man's silhouette. Kneeling on the edge of the bed, Sarah's eyes plotted the shape's relentless progress. She had never been more terrified in her life and felt a strong urge to run out of the bedroom, but that would mean stepping over the crawling shadow … She had no time to think of an alternative escape route, because the shadow suddenly reared up from the carpet and instantly materialised into the three-dimensional solid form of a man wearing a long black robe of some sort. Weak with terror, Sarah threw up her arms defensively as she collapsed back on to the bed, and then everything went black.

The next thing she knew it was almost four o'clock in the morning and she had no recollection of what had happened in the interim. Her whole body felt limp and weak, so much so that she could hardly draw breath, and her head slumped inert on the pillow until the light of dawn seeped into the room. She eventually managed to crawl from her bed at 10 o'clock the following morning and could hear her cousin Lisa chatting to her aunt downstairs. She had called to help look after her Aunt Esther and had tried to wake Sarah several times without success and was beginning to worry that she was ill, when she saw her stagger downstairs, as white as a sheet.

"Sarah! What on earth's the matter? I've been trying to wake you for the last hour. Are you ill? You look awful."

"I don't know … I just feel a bit weak … and diz … diz …" her voice trailed away and she crumpled to the floor.

"Quick, auntie! Ring for an ambulance, Sarah's collapsed."

The ambulance arrived and Sarah was rushed to hospital. On the way, she came round and tried to explain how she felt to the paramedics, but she barely had the energy to get the words out.

"Just lie quietly, love. We'll soon get you sorted out."

At the hospital Sarah underwent a series of tests, the results of which were all inconclusive and she was subsequently diagnosed with a type of chronic-fatigue syndrome, thought to have been brought on by over-exertion in caring for her sick aunt. Sarah disputed the diagnosis because she had felt absolutely fine until that night and exhaustion is something which creeps up gradually. She was the first to admit that caring for her aunt was tiring, but she was a healthy young woman, well capable of a bit of hard work. She had another theory which was far less mundane. She tried to explain her conviction that something had somehow siphoned off all the energy from her body. She was rather vague, claiming it had something to do with a 'ghost' that had entered her bedroom from under the door, and the medical staff took no notice, putting her confused ramblings down to her poor physical state.

On leaving hospital, Sarah returned to her parents' house on Crombey Street, about a half a mile from her aunt's house, to recuperate. With lots of care and attention from her parents, she slowly began to regain her strength, although they often noticed that she had a haunted look on her face and had developed a morbid fear of the dark.

Then the sinister apparition manifested once again.

This time, Sarah did not pass out when the entity materialised out of thin air and so was able to remember everything about it in great detail. Not only that, the incident was also witnessed by her seventeen-year-old brother Russell.

At 9.45pm, on Wednesday, 12 August 1981, Russell came into his sister's bedroom pestering her for money for fish and chips. He found his sister sitting at her dressing table putting on her make-up.

"How many times have I told you to knock before barging into my room?" she yelled. "Can't you see I'm busy?"

Their parents sitting in the lounge downstairs looked at each other and sighed. They had often bemoaned the fact that most of the conversations between their two children were conducted at maximum volume.

"Chill, sis," laughed Russell. "How's about some fish and chips? I fetch – you pay."

"Get lost, greedy guts! You've got hollow legs. It's not long since you had your tea and anyway, I thought you were on a diet."

"I know, but I'm a growing lad. Go on, sis. Be a sport. I'm starving"

The conversation stopped right there, because, at that moment, they both witnessed the appearance of a tall man in a long black cloak who seemed to materialise in a flash from the side of the wardrobe. It was back! Summoning all her strength, Sarah flung her hairdryer at the phantom before rushing headlong out of the bedroom with Russell in close pursuit. They ran screaming downstairs and into the living room where their parents shook their heads in disbelief. Would they never grow up?

"What the heck's the matter now?" asked their father, exasperated. "We're trying to watch the telly in peace. Is that too much to ask?"

"It's time you two grew up," sighed their mother. "You behave like a couple of two-year-olds the minute you get together."

"But, Mum," said Sarah, visibly shaking. "It's him again. That man I told you about. And Russell saw him too. Didn't you, Rus?"

"Yeah! He was really creepy and had on this kind of long black cloak.

He just appeared out of nowhere. Weird!"

The fact that brother and sister were actually agreeing about something, made their parents sit up and listen.

"What man? What are you talking about?" asked their father, still annoyed at having his favourite soap disrupted.

"That one I told you about at Aunt Esther's. The one that made me ill."

"Alright, calm down the pair of you. Let's go and take a look," he said, suddenly realising that this was no teenage prank; Sarah and Russell were genuinely terrified by what they had seen and Sarah had been definitely very poorly since the last episode; not her usual self at all.

Their parents ran upstairs to investigate, but found nothing amiss in Sarah's room – just the usual untidy mess. There was certainly no sign of any intruder, cloaked or otherwise.

"Nothing there, just as I thought," said their father. "I think all this has got a bit out of hand. People can't just appear and disappear now can they? I'm sure you'll feel better, Sarah, when you've had a bit more of your mum's home cooking and tlc."

"Yes, come here, love. You've just got a bit over-tired, that's all. Russell, how about going and getting those fish and chips. Here's a fiver."

Despite all her parents' reassurances, Sarah still felt very jittery and was even more nervous of sleeping in her bedroom after that night's encounter. However, she need not have worried because, thankfully, the menacing figure never bothered her again. The apparition was never identified, and seems to have been some type of vampiric being that had been siphoning off her vitality. It is possible that the entity is still at large and capable of seeking out fresh involuntary blood donors!

These vampires that draw off the very life-force of their victims are reminiscent of the incubus and succubus of Judaeo-Christian belief. An incubus is a male demonic being that lies on top of female sleepers at night and sexually abuses them. It also drains the victim of energy so that she is incapable of resisting, or calling out for help. The incubus often takes on the form of an attractive young human male, whereas its female counterpart – the succubus – often resembles a voluptuous, attractive woman. There are other nocturnal entities haunting our bedrooms, and the most widely-reported of these is known as the 'Old Hag'.

'Old Hag Syndrome' has been recognised by psychologists for many years, but no one is sure whether the cause is supernatural, or simply the product of a semi-conscious mind. Victims wake up in bed to find that they cannot move a muscle, even though their sense of sight, touch, taste and smell are still intact. They often experience the sensation of a great weight bearing down on their chest and intuitively know that there is a sinister or evil presence in the room. This presence sometimes manifests itself as an old hag with evil-looking eyes, hence the name of this syndrome.

In the Clutches of the Evil Hag

In 2003, twenty-seven-year-old Tony woke at his home in the Kensington district of Liverpool, Merseyside, at three o'clock in the morning and found himself unable to move a muscle in any part of his body. He panicked as he struggled to breathe, then opened his eyes – and saw an old woman wearing a black shawl leaning over him. She started to cackle, and stroked Tony's face with what felt like long bony fingers. The night visitor's face was sinister and threatening and she was muttering dark and unintelligible words. She leaned forward and began to kiss Tony on the lips with her own loathsome, wrinkled lips, and the foul stench of decay filled his nostrils and made him want to retch. Summoning all his willpower, he tried desperately to regain the power of movement, and he suddenly screamed out and was able to push away the eerie figure. When he sat up, the old hag was nowhere to be seen.

Six days later, there was a second Old Hag report about two miles from the first incident, this time involving forty-five-year-old George, also from Liverpool.

Feeling very tired one evening, he had retired to bed at 10pm, leaving his wife downstairs, finishing off some ironing. She said she would be coming up to bed in about an hour. However, at around 11 o'clock that night, George was awakened by someone climbing into the bed. Naturally assuming that it was his wife, he turned over to give her a cuddle, only to find that there was no one there. George thought that perhaps he had been dreaming, and turned over to try and get back to sleep. As he was about to drop off again, he felt a tremendous weight pushing down on his chest, stopping him breathing. He opened his eyes and found himself paralysed from head to toe – only his eyelids still moved. An amorphous dark shape was on top of him. George later stated that he felt as if the presence was squeezing the life out of him, and that if he didn't fight it with all his strength, he would surely die.

An unsightly wizened face leant over his and as the ancient face came closer, every leathery wrinkle and every blackened pore came into focus. Above all, the evil staring eyes, in which there was a flickering golden light, seemed to penetrate the very depths of his being. The face came closer still, until the old hag put her withered slavering mouth to George's mouth, forcing him to taste her rancid breath, which seemed to fill his head with the odour of putrefaction. George had always classed himself as an atheist, but that night he inwardly called upon God to save him from the clutches of the evil hag. As his thoughts focused into prayer, the grossly lined face grimaced as if in great pain, and the eyes turned completely white.

The weight slowly lifted from George, allowing his lungs to expand once more. He drew in great gulps of air as the hag vanished into the night. George then felt movement returning to his big toe, then the whole of his leg and then life quickly flooded back into the rest of his body. He managed to raise himself up into a sitting position, leaning against the bed's headboard, where he sat gasping for breath, his heart pounding for several minutes. He looked about him, and saw to his relief that the room was now empty. As soon as he was able, he ran down the stairs to tell his wife about the whole ghastly experience. She immediately noticed a strong putrescent odour, and sniffed his mouth. She backed away, grimacing in disgust. To George, this was proof that the hag had been no mere dream or apparition. He gargled with antiseptic mouthwash and scrubbed his teeth repeatedly, until he was finally rid of the last horrid vestiges of the old hag's repulsive kiss.

There were two further incidents of this kind, reported days later in other areas of Merseyside, and both victims of these eerie assaults gave a carbon copy description of the old hag who had terrorised the two men in the earlier cases. The victims particularly stressed that their nostrils had been assaulted by an overpowering and revolting odour during the attacks, the likes of which they had never smelt before or since.

Weeks after these four cases, there came a cluster of reports of the Old Hag in the neighbouring county of Cheshire, and herein lies a peculiarity of this phenomenon; Old Hag Syndrome is rarely a widespread occurrence, but rather, a number of highly localised incidents are reported, sometimes in the same street, and this is difficult to explain in terms of traditional psychology. Suggestion and hysteria could undoubtedly be cited as the cause, if two or more people knew about the hag being reported several doors away, for example. However, it has been found that in most cases, people have not discussed the matter with their neighbours. The most common response in the aftermath of such an attack is to seek medical help and doctors, of course, are duty bound to treat such reports by patients in the strictest confidence.

So, is the hag just the modern manifestation of a type of vampire that has been at large for centuries? What purpose would the hag's assaults serve, if she was not vampiric? How and why does she drain people of their energy and the power of movement? Could she be some type of parasitic entity, rather than the demonic being that most occultists believe her to be?

Living Nightmare

In 1992, there was a classic case of a psychic vampire reported in Cardiff. Thirty-four-year-old secretary Jane Williams was suffering from recurring nightmares, which featured a man in black floating in through her bedroom window each night. In the dreams, the man would put his mouth to Jane's lips and literally suck the breath from her lungs until she woke up, gasping for air.

After a week of such nightmares, Jane woke up trembling one night in her Wharton Street home to find the shadowy outline of a man hovering above her bed. She let out a scream and the weird apparition dissolved before her eyes. The man in the nightmares had a very distinctive face, with unusually dark menacing eyes and a white-streaked quiff.

One afternoon, in October 1992, Jane was returning from work when

31

she encountered the same man on Queen Street. She stopped in her tracks when she recognised her nocturnal tormentor, and before she turned to run off, he uttered something sinister but unintelligible under his breath. Jane suffered two further nightmares at the house on Wharton Street, and on both occasions, she awoke gasping for breath and feeling completely exhausted.

Jane then went to stay at her sister Claudia's home in Caerphilly, and after two nights of peaceful sleep, the nightmares returned with a vengeance. Jane awoke screaming in the spare bedroom and her sister ran to her aid. On entering the bedroom, Claudia saw a dark indistinct shape, almost like a cloud of black smoke, rolling along just under the ceiling and then vanishing into the folds of the drawn curtains. A Methodist lay-preacher was finally enlisted to tackle the supernatural villain, and it was found that as long as Jane kept a crucifix at her bedside, she was not troubled by either the nightmares or the accompanying assaults by the man in black. The lay preacher believed the invader to be a demon, but the symptoms which Jane described actually bore all the hallmarks of a psychic vampire attack: shortness of breath, complete exhaustion, and a sensation of dread.

Attic Attack

An almost identical meeting with a vaporous vampiric being took place on a housing estate in Exeter, in 2005, only on this occasion, the apparition was said to be wearing a tuxedo! The victim was once again female, and the attack took place at around 11pm under the eaves of her house in the attic. Sandra, the thirty-nine-year-old mother of two teenaged children, Becky, aged thirteen, and Zara, aged fifteen, had converted the attic into a study. It was lined with bookshelves and there was a computer for all three of them to use.

Sandra's daughters used the den to surf the net most evenings, but one Sunday night, when Becky and Zara were sound asleep in bed, Sandra decided to send an email to a friend from the attic computer. As she sat typing out the email, she suddenly felt as if something was in the attic with her. A floorboard creaked and she felt goosebumps rise involuntarily on her arms. She distinctly heard someone sighing quite close to her, and suddenly, out of the corner of her eye, she saw a man in a black dinner jacket and matching trousers standing within reach of her. He wore a bow tie and his thick hair was dark and slicked back. Sandra was instantly paralysed and she could hear her heart pounding as she sat at the computer, unable to move.

The stranger's abnormally large coal black eyes stood out like saucers in his deathly pale face. The effect was electrifying. He silently stepped forward towards Sandra and feverishly began to kiss her neck and face. With each kiss, she felt as if the ghoulish man was literally drawing her very life from her. All her strength evaporated, leaving her as weak as a newborn baby. Her head spun, she started to feel sick and dizzy and then began to lose consciousness. When she came round, about twenty-five minutes later, she found herself sprawled on the attic floor. She looked around and found the dark stranger gone.

Sandra told her best friend Julie about her odd experience. Julie worked as a tutor at the local university, and she in turn told an amateur investigator of the paranormal, Allan Moore. He claimed that the unearthly life-draining ghost in the dinner jacket was a type of psychic vampire who had been preying on people in the Topsham Road area – the neighbourhood where Sandra lived. Sandra's daughters were not told about the man in the tuxedo because she didn't want to alarm them, so Sandra shuddered when both girls reported seeing the silhouette of a man against the blinds of their bedroom in the early hours of the morning.

Allan Moore resorted to the traditional remedies for protecting victims against vampires; he scattered garlic bulbs, crucifixes and bottles of holy water about the attic and bedrooms of Sandra's home, and these measures seemed to do the trick, because the man in the tuxedo with the chalk-white face was seen no more by Sandra and her daughters.

The cases of vampires of the life-force documented so far within this chapter occurred in this century and the last one, but some of the most terrifying incidents of this kind were first recorded in nineteenth century London.

Sekhmet – Vampiress of Ancient Egypt

Standing sixty-eight feet high on London's Thames Embankment, is a 180-ton obelisk of red granite that dates back fourteen centuries to the reign of Thutmose III, the sixth Pharaoh of the Eighteenth Dynasty. This tall, tapering four-sided monument, which ends in a pyramidal top, never had anything to do with Queen Cleopatra VII of Egypt, yet the obelisk is popularly known as 'Cleopatra's Needle' for some reason. In 1819, Mehemet Ali, the Viceroy of Egypt, presented the needle to Britain to commemorate the victorious battles of Nelson and Abercromby. However, the obelisk remained at Alexandria in Egypt until 1877, when the first attempt was made to ship it to England.

The obelisk was laboriously dug out of the sands that had covered the bulk of it for over a thousand years. Many of the Egyptian labourers involved in the excavation believed that something evil was residing in the needle, for superstitions were rife in that part of Egypt about Sekhmet – a fierce vampiress who was worshipped by a blood-drinking cult dating back thousands of years to the Twelfth Dynasty. Sekhmet was originally known as the Egyptian goddess of war, but even in times of peace she was feared because of her notorious blood-lust.

She was depicted as a female with a lion's mane, a beautiful pale face with large black piercing eyes, and a fanged mouth. She was always robed in scarlet and was known by various titles, such as The Mistress of Dread and the Lady of Slaughter. In the ancient myths, Sekhmet was fabled to have come close to destroying the whole of mankind on one occasion, because of her insatiable blood-lust. Ra, the sun-god of Upper Egypt, was said to have tricked her into drinking a blood-like liquid, which was in fact pomegranate juice mixed with beer. The vampire goddess then fell into a long slumber and was finally transformed into the gentle deity Hathor.

However, the truth behind this allegorical tale is much more sinister. Sekhmet was said to have been temporarily 'tamed' by Egyptian High Priests who used Sumerian exorcism rites. It was said that only the wraith, or psychic shell of Sekhmet survived the exorcism, and that the feeble but deadly vestige of this violent lover of blood had sought sanctuary in the fallen obelisk of Thutmose III.

On 14 October 1877, the ship carrying the massive structure to England, nearly capsized during a fierce storm in the Bay of Biscay, and six lives were lost as a result. The obelisk was spared and finally arrived in England in January 1878, where it was subsequently erected on the Victoria Embankment in September of that year. Hidden within the pedestal of Cleopatra's Needle there is a rather interesting time capsule from Victorian times containing a full set of British Empire coins, a rupee, a three-inch model of the monument and plans of the obelisk on velum, plus a Bradshaw Railway Guide booklet, a shilling razor, a portrait of Queen Victoria, a box of cigars, a collection of children's toys, and twelve photographs of the most beautiful women of the day.

A naked man was seen jumping into the Thames close to the obelisk, weeks after its erection. The body of the suicide victim was later recovered from the river but never identified. Not long after this, rumours began to circulate about a malevolent power emanating from Cleopatra's Needle, which could cause people to jump to their deaths in the Thames. One such unfortunate was Miss Davies, a twenty-seven-year-old Pimlico woman, who left her home one night in 1880 and wandered about the streets of London in a morose trance. Upon reaching the Victorian Embankment, she felt a powerful 'magnetic' force drawing her to the obelisk, where she heard the eerie sounds of female laughter. Davies found herself walking towards the ancient monolith, unable to control her legs. She felt compelled to jump into the dark swirling current and would have drowned had it not been for the young vagrant who dragged her back on to dry land.

Miss Davies gradually recovered from her ordeal in hospital, but suffered terrible nightmares in which there appeared an abnormally tall woman in dark red robes with a terrifying white face and black almond-shaped eyes. Each time this disturbing figure appeared in her dreams, Miss Davies would find herself paralysed with fear, and the entity would slowly open an enormous mouth to reveal a vast array of needle-sharp teeth. The figure would then move steadily towards the dreamer and bite into her face, tearing off strips of her flesh. Fortunately, the nightmares ended after a fortnight, but Miss Davies believed the cannibalistic woman was not merely a figment of her dreaming mind, but something truly evil connected with the obelisk on the Embankment.

Could the woman in the scarlet robes have been the vampiric goddess Sekhmet? Many men and women from all classes and walks of life have since chosen to end their lives by jumping into the River Thames close to Cleopatra's Needle, and even the police have remarked on the seeming attraction of the suicide spot. Could it be that the ancient vampiress is still exerting her dark powers even today, by actually encouraging people to drown themselves in order to access their life-energy?

Early English Vampires

OF ALL THE FORMS of interaction between the living and the dead, visitation by a vampire is the most loathsome. Some occultists debate whether a vampire is truly alive – in the normal sense of the term – that is with a conscious mind of the type that you and I possess. Or is it only as 'alive' as say, a parasitic virus, for example, or a bloodthirsty mosquito that is devoid of any conscience, and whose sole purpose is to siphon off the life-blood of its human host. My personal belief is that vampires have varying degrees of consciousness, ranging from the extremely limited type of perception that a maggot, say, might have of its surroundings, right up to the complex standards of awareness that are characteristic of the human mind.

Of course, some people simply believe that vampires do not exist at all, based on what they vaguely term 'common sense'. Religious people may believe that a man cannot rise from his grave after dark, yet accept that the founder of Christianity did just such a thing at the Resurrection. Of course, that is not to say that Jesus was a vampire, but it does throw some light on the way our belief system works.

It would seem from the large amount of data that I have accumulated on vampires, that they are mostly cryptobiotic – that is to say, they possess an ametabolic state of life which responds to environmental conditions such as freezing, desiccation, and even oxygen deficiency. In other words, the vampire could possibly survive underwater, could live much longer in hostile desert conditions than the most robust of humans, and could even be revived after years of being encased in ice.

This cryptobiosis is evident in some of the lower organisms such as the incredible tardigrade, a tiny segmented creature that looks like a microscopic bear with its bulky body and four pairs of stumpy legs and claws. Tardigrades can be found in hot springs, in the snows of the Himalayas, or at the bottom of the deepest ocean. They can even endure an intense bombardment of X-rays (up to one thousand times the lethal human dose). Not only can the tardigrade survive in the vacuum of space, it can also suspend its metabolism indefinitely through dehydration and come back to life decades later.

In recent years, a piece of moss in a museum was rehydrated after one hundred and seventy years and tardigrades from the 1880s were found to have successfully revived themselves. Scientists are currently studying the humble tardigrade to see if they can learn how to store human organs designated for transplants for much longer periods. The DNA of these incredible creatures is also being scrutinised with a view to understanding how it might one day be possible to create a human being who could be both as resilient to ageing and disease and virtually immortal as the tardigrade.

It is possible to speculate whether nature has already combined the genetic codes of a branch of the human tree with that of a DNA akin to the tardigrade – and produced the vampire as a result. Strange skulls, with grossly overdeveloped fangs, have been found buried in the earth, which refuse to be pigeon-holed as pro-simian, or proto-human, by anthropologists. The theory of evolution maintains that all the plants and animals existing today are descended from species that existed before them. In 1859, Charles Darwin introduced a very controversial theory about the origins of the human race in his landmark book, *Origin of Species* in which he argued that homo sapiens were descendants of an ape-like ancestor.

Once accepted, Darwin's theory of evolution became the new orthodoxy, opposed only by cranks and fundamentalists. In recent years, however, it has been questioned by a new generation of freethinkers, who have pointed out many weak points in the Darwinian hypothesis. Over three hundred and twelve physical traits have been identified which set humans apart from apes and chimpanzees. Such things as our virtual hairlessness have to be taken into consideration, along with our upright way of walking, the complete helplessness of human infancy, our lengthy childhood, and the biggest problem confronting Darwin's theory: the human brain.

The human brain is one forty-fifth of our body weight, whereas the gorilla has a brain that is only one two-hundredth of its body weight.

With the sole exception of the dolphin, our brain is bigger in gross size than that of any other mammal. According to Darwin, nature never over-endows a creature with more than its basic requirements, yet the cubic capacity of the human brain (which ranges from 1,200 to 1,800cc) is far in excess of the size needed for everyday survival and procreation. If we accept that Nature never over-endows a species beyond the demands of its everyday existence, why then does the human brain have faculties and a cubic capacity far beyond its needs? According to Darwinian theory, mankind should only concern itself with hunting, survival and procreation, yet we engage in such things as poetry, art, music and literature – activities that are a superfluous luxury in our day-to-day struggle for survival. There are even those geniuses amongst us, who are endowed with sufficient brain capacity to land astronauts on the moon and split the atom, but where did that incredible brainpower come from?

Darwin's theory has no answer to that question. So what if Darwin was wrong? What if mankind *was* created by a higher intelligence, after all, as many religions claim, and, rather than evolving, perhaps there were different versions and prototypes of human beings; those that were active by day, and those that preferred the hours of darkness to go about their business. We could call these two contrasting versions of homo sapiens diurnals (daytime people) and nocturnals (night-time people) and we all know people who fit into each category.

For thousands of years, the nocturnal vampire is said to have existed in one form or another, and according to ancient occult lore, one of the earliest recorded vampires was Lilith, the first wife of Adam – as described in the Talmud. In this alternative version of Genesis, God created Lilith, not from the dust from which he had fashioned Adam, but from filth and sediment. Adam and Lilith never found peace together as a couple; for when he wished to lie down with her, she took offence at the recumbent posture that he demanded. "Why must I lie beneath you?" she complained, and reminded Adam of their common origins: "I also was made from dust, and am therefore your equal." Because Adam tried to enforce her obedience, Lilith uttered the magic name of God in a rage, then rose into the air and left him to be with Lucifer. In essence then, the quarrel was simply this; that Lilith preferred to stand over Adam, but God wanted the male to be the dominant one in the relationship.

"I have been deserted by my helpmeet," Adam complained to his Creator, and God at once sent forth the angels Senoy, Sansenoy and Semangelof to fetch Lilith back, and at the Red Sea, which was surrounded by a region full of lascivious demons, they finally found her. Lilith gave birth to the Lilim at the rate of more than one hundred a day. It is possible that these ancient legends are referring to the early origins of the vampire.

This book is about the vampires of England, and some of the earliest references to the bloodthirsty undead are to be found in the works of two medieval writers, Walter Map and William of Newburgh. Walter Map (c.1137-1209) was a Welsh poet and ecclesiastic who had studied at the University of Paris and who had also became a prominent clerk in the royal household of Henry II. He wrote down the many anecdotes and trivia he had accumulated during his travels in his *De Nugis Curialium* (Trifles of Courtiers). This work contained a mixed bag of bizarre stories dealing with such subjects as demonic infanticide, the capture of Jerusalem by Saladin, a comparison of the royal courts with Hell, one of the early kings of Portugal who had his wife murdered, and amongst Map's satirical writings and accounts of court gossip, there are also several early tales of English vampires.

The Wicked Man of Hereford

Writing in the twelfth century, Map recounts the curious story of a 'wicked man' of Hereford who rose from his grave after dark to wander the streets, crying out the names of people he had known when he was alive. These people would then become stricken with a mysterious fever and die within three days. Gilbert Foliot, Bishop of Hereford (and later Bishop of London) was consulted on the matter. He pronounced that the ghoul was a vampire revenant – a corpse animated by the Devil – and he promptly gave specific instructions to a band of his men to lay the creature to rest permanently, saying, "Dig up the body and cut off the head with a spade, then sprinkle it with holy water and rebury it."

This was attempted, but the vampire put up a mighty struggle. The holy water had no marked effect and the vampire's spinal column proved too difficult for them to sever. The creature drunkenly staggered about for a while, before crawling back into its open grave to lick its wounds. Before the vampire could claw the earth back over its temporary resting place, one of the villagers was brave enough to make a last-ditch attempt at killing it. With all his might he brought down the blade of his sword on the writhing revenant, splitting open its skull, which fell apart like a ripe melon. The vampire gave out one last strange guttural sound before slumping face down into its grave for good. Holy water and vinegar were then liberally sprinkled on the grave, which was later marked with a Christian cross to prevent the fiend from rising again.

Baby Killer

In another of the chapters of *De Nugis Curialium* Walter Map recounts another chilling tale of a vampiric demon, in which a knight discovers that his newborn baby has had its throat cut from ear to ear, just hours after its birth. The knight recoils in horror at the sight of his first born child lying dead in its blood-soaked cradle. His unstinting efforts to find and capture the perpetrator of the evil deed were all in vain, for he had left not a single clue. The same grisly fate befell the knight's next two children shortly after their births, and so, after the birth of the fourth child, a mass vigil was kept near the child's bedchamber. Torches were lit all over the household and many of the knight's friends and relatives stayed up to keep a close watch on the room where the newborn babe was sleeping in his cradle.

That night, an impoverished stranger arrived at the knight's house seeking hospitality. He was invited in to enjoy a drink, a simple meal, and a place by the fireside, for which he was very grateful. Hearing of the tragedy of the three dead babies, and wanting to repay the knight for his kindness, the stranger offered to join the vigil and remain awake all night to keep watch on the newborn baby. One by one, as the early hours of the morning crawled by, the other people of the vigil started to fall asleep, one by one, until only the stranger was left awake. He kept his word and refused to succumb to drowsiness.

In the early hours of the morning, the guest watched as a very respectable looking matron suddenly appeared in the room, silently stepping over the sleepers who were sprawled all over the floor. She crept across the room like a mouse, looking about her as she went. The stranger pretended to be asleep like the others, but he was watching the woman's every movement through half-closed eyes. Soon, the matron was standing by the cradle. As she hunched over it she suddenly grasped the baby by its tiny throat. The guest rushed across the room to apprehend the woman, raising the alarm as he did so, and waking the people who had lapsed into slumber.

He clung like a limpet to this cruel and murderous woman as she wrestled to be free of him, when, all of a sudden, her double entered the room. Not only were the newcomer's facial features identical to her own but so too were the clothes she wore. The stranger was evidently a very knowledgeable and perceptive man and he immediately grasped what was going on. Addressing the knight and his confused household he declared: "There can be no doubt that the lady who has now come is very virtuous and very dear to heaven, and that by her good works she has stirred hell and provoked the anger of devils against her, and so this evil messenger of theirs, this loathsome instrument of their wrath, has been fashioned as far as possible in the likeness of this noble lady, that this demon may cause this noble soul to be accused of the guilt of her heinous deeds. And in order that you may believe, see what she will do after I release her."

The stranger then let go of the struggling doppelganger, whereupon she raised up her arms and then her body seemed to melt and transform itself into some kind of winged creature, which frantically flapped its great wings and then made its escape through the open window. This was one of the earliest accounts of a shape-shifting vampire of the kind that would be reported again many times in the following centuries.

William of Newburgh (1136-1208), English chronicler and Canon of the Augustinian priory at Newburgh in the North Riding of Yorkshire, was one of the chief authorities on the reign of Henry II. Within his work, *Historia Rerum Anglicarum* (History of English Affairs), which covers the period from 1066 to 1198, there are three intriguing accounts of vampiric beings, in Chapters 22, 23 and 24 of Book 5, and they are reproduced here:

The Dead Man Who Wandered About

In these days a wonderful event befell in the county of Buckingham, which I, in the first instance, partially heard from certain friends, and was afterwards more fully informed of by Stephen, the venerable archdeacon of that province.

A certain man died, and, according to custom, by the honourable exertion of his wife and kindred, was laid in the tomb on the eve of the Lord's Ascension. On the following night, however, having entered the bed where his wife was reposing, he not only terrified her on awaking, but nearly crushed her by the insupportable weight of his body. The next night, also, he afflicted the astonished woman in the same manner, who, frightened at the danger, as the struggle of the third night drew near, took care to remain awake herself, and surround herself with watchful companions. Still he came; but being repulsed by the shouts of the watchers, and seeing that he was prevented from doing mischief, he departed.

Thus driven off from his wife, he harassed in a similar manner his own brothers, who were dwelling in the same street; but they, following the cautious example of the woman, passed the nights in wakefulness with their companions, ready to meet and repel the expected danger. He appeared, notwithstanding, as if with the hope of surprising them should they be overcome with drowsiness; but being repelled by the carefulness and valour of the watchers, he rioted among the animals, both indoors and outdoors, as their wildness and unwonted movements testified.

Having thus become a like serious nuisance to his friends and neighbours, he imposed upon all the same necessity for nocturnal watchfulness; and in that very street a general watch was kept in every house, each being fearful of his approach unawares. After having for some time rioted in this manner during the night-time alone, he began to wander abroad in daylight, formidable indeed to all, but visible only to a few; for oftentimes, on his encountering a number of persons, he would appear to one or two only, though at the same time his presence was not concealed from the rest.

At length the inhabitants, alarmed beyond measure, thought it advisable to seek the counsel of the church; and they detailed the whole affair, with tearful lamentation, to the above-mentioned archdeacon, at a meeting of the clergy over which he was solemnly presiding. Whereupon he immediately intimated in writing the whole circumstances of the case to the venerable bishop of Lincoln, who was then resident in London, whose opinion and judgment on so unwonted a matter he was very properly of opinion should be waited for: but the bishop, being amazed at his account, held a searching investigation with his companions; and there were some who said that such things had often befallen in England, and cited frequent examples to show that tranquillity could not be restored to the people until the body of this most wretched man were dug up and burnt. This proceeding, however, appeared indecent and improper in the last degree to the reverend bishop, who, shortly after, addressed a letter of absolution, written with his own hand, to the archdeacon, in order that it might be demonstrated by inspection in what state the body of that man really was; and he commanded his tomb to be opened, and the letter having been laid upon his breast, to be again closed: so the sepulchre having been opened, the corpse was found as it had been placed there, and the charter of absolution having been deposited upon its breast, and the tomb once more closed, he was thenceforth never more seen to wander, nor permitted to inflict annoyance or terror upon any one.

A Similar Occurrence at Berwick

In the northern parts of England, also, we know that another event, not unlike this and equally wonderful, happened about the same time. At the mouth of the River Tweed, and in the jurisdiction of the King of Scotland, there stands a noble city which is called Berwick. In this town a certain man, very wealthy, but as it afterwards appeared, a great rogue, having been buried, after his death sallied forth (by the contrivance, as it is believed, of Satan) out of his grave by night, and was borne hither and thither, pursued by a pack of dogs with loud barkings; thus striking great terror into the neighbours, and returning to his tomb before daylight.

After this had continued for several days, and no one dared to be found out of doors after dusk – for each dreaded an encounter with this deadly monster – the higher and middle classes of the people held a necessary investigation into what was requisite to be done; the more simple among them fearing, in the event of negligence, to be soundly beaten by this prodigy of the grave; but the wiser shrewdly concluding that were a remedy further delayed, the atmosphere, infected and corrupted by the constant whirlings through it of the pestiferous corpse, would engender disease and death to a great extent; the necessity of providing against which was shown by frequent examples in similar cases.

They, therefore, procured ten young men renowned for boldness, who were to dig up the horrible carcass, and, having cut it limb from limb, reduce it into food and fuel for the flames. When this was done, the commotion ceased. Moreover, it is stated that the monster, while it was being borne about (as it is said) by Satan, had told certain persons whom it had by chance encountered, that as long as it remained unburned, the people should have no peace. Being burnt, tranquillity appeared to be restored to them; but a pestilence, which arose in consequence, carried off the greater portion of them: for never did it so furiously rage elsewhere, though it was at that time general throughout all the borders of England, as shall be more fully explained in its proper place.

In the chapter that follows this, William documents the ghoulish activities and violent end of a vampiric friar.

Of Certain Prodigies

It would not be easy to believe that the corpses of the dead should sally (I know not by what agency) from their graves, and should wander about to the terror or destruction of the living, and again return to the tomb, which of its own accord spontaneously opened to receive them, did not frequent examples, occurring in our own times, suffice to establish this fact, to the truth of which there is abundant testimony. It would be strange if such things should have happened formerly, since we can find no evidence of them in the works of ancient authors, whose vast labour it was to commit to writing every occurrence worthy of memory; for if they never neglected to register even events of moderate interest, how could they have suppressed a fact at once so amazing and horrible, supposing it to have happened in their day? Moreover, were I to write down all the instances of this kind which I have ascertained to have befallen in our times, the undertaking would be beyond measure laborious and troublesome; so I will fain add two more only (and these of recent occurrence) to those I have already narrated, and insert them in our history, as occasion offers, as a warning to posterity.

A few years ago the chaplain of a certain illustrious lady, casting off mortality, was consigned to the tomb in that noble monastery which is called Melrose. This man, having little respect for the sacred order to which he belonged, was excessively secular in his pursuits, and – what especially blackens his reputation as a minister of the holy sacrament – so addicted to the vanity of the chase as to be designated by many by the infamous title of "Hundeprest" or the dog-priest; and this occupation, during his lifetime, was either laughed at by men, or considered in a worldly view; but after his death – as the event showed – the guiltiness of it was brought to light: for, issuing from the grave at night-time, he was prevented by the meritorious resistance of its holy inmates from injuring or terrifying anyone within the monastery itself; whereupon he wandered beyond the walls, and hovered chiefly, with loud groans and horrible murmurs, round the bedchamber of his former mistress. She, after this had frequently occurred, becoming exceedingly terrified, revealed her fears or danger to one of the friars who visited her about the business of the monastery; demanding with tears that prayers more earnest than usual should be poured out to the Lord in her behalf, as for one in agony. With whose anxiety the friar — for she appeared deserving of the best endeavours, on the part of the holy convent of that place, by her frequent donations to it — piously and justly sympathised, and promised a speedy remedy through the mercy of the Most High Provider for all.

Thereupon, returning to the monastery, he obtained the companionship of another friar, of equally determined spirit, and two powerful young men, with whom he intended with constant vigilance to keep guard over the cemetery where that miserable priest lay buried. These four, therefore, furnished with arms and animated with courage, passed the night in that place, safe in the assistance which each afforded to the other. Midnight had now passed by, and no monster appeared; upon which it came to pass that three of the party, leaving him only who had sought their company on the spot, departed into the nearest house, for the purpose, as they averred, of warming themselves, for the night was cold. As soon as this man was left alone in this place, the devil, imagining that he had found the right moment for breaking his courage, incontinently roused up his own chosen vessel, who appeared to have reposed longer than usual. Having beheld this from afar, he grew stiff with terror by reason of his being alone; but soon recovering his courage, and no place of refuge being at hand, he valiantly withstood the onset of the fiend, who came rushing upon him with a terrible noise, and he struck the axe which he wielded in his hand deep into his body. On receiving this wound, the monster groaned aloud, and turning his back, fled with a rapidity not at all interior to that with which he had advanced, while the admirable man urged his flying foe from behind, and compelled him to seek his own tomb again; which opening of its own accord, and receiving its guest from the advance of the pursuer, immediately appeared to close again with the same facility. In the meantime, they who, impatient of the coldness of the night, had retreated to the fire, ran up, though somewhat too late, and, having heard what had happened, rendered needful assistance in digging up and removing from the midst of the tomb the accursed corpse at the earliest dawn. When they had divested it of the clay cast forth with it, they found the huge wound it had received, and a great quantity of gore which had flowed from it in the sepulchre; and so having carried it away beyond the walls of the monastery and burnt it, they scattered the ashes to the winds. These things I have explained in a simple narration, as I myself heard them recounted by religious men.

Another event, also, not unlike this, but more pernicious in its effects, happened at the castle which is called Anantis, as I have heard from an aged monk who lived in honour and authority in those parts, and who related this event as having occurred in his own presence. A certain man of evil conduct flying, through fear of his enemies or the law, out of the province of York, to the lord of the before-named castle, took up his abode there, and having cast upon a service befitting his humour, laboured hard to increase rather than correct his own evil propensities. He married a wife, to his own ruin indeed, as it afterwards appeared; for, hearing certain rumours respecting her, he was vexed with the spirit of Jealousy. Anxious to ascertain the truth of these reports, he pretended to be going on a journey from which he would not return for some days; but coming back in the evening, he was privily introduced into his bedroom by a maid-servant, who was in the secret, and lay hidden on a beam overhanging his wife's chamber, that he might prove with his own eyes if anything were done to the dishonour of his marriage-bed. Thereupon beholding his wife in the act of fornication with a young man of the neighbourhood, and in his indignation forgetful of his purpose, he fell, and was dashed heavily to the ground, near where they were lying.

The adulterer himself leaped up and escaped; but the wife, cunningly dissembling the fact, busied herself in gently raising her fallen husband from the earth. As soon as he had partially recovered, he upbraided her with her adultery, and threatened punishment; but she answering, "Explain yourself, my lord," said she; "you are speaking unbecomingly which must be imputed not to you, but to the sickness with which you are troubled." Being much shaken by the fall, and his whole body stupefied, he was attacked with a disease, insomuch that the man whom I have mentioned as having related these facts to me visiting him in the pious discharge of his duties, admonished him to make confession of his sins, and receive the Christian Eucharist in proper form: but as he was occupied in thinking about what had happened to him, and what his wife had said, put off the wholesome advice until the morrow — that morrow which in this world he was fated never to behold! — for the next night, destitute of Christian grace, and a prey to his well-earned misfortunes, he shared the deep slumber of death.

A Christian burial, indeed, he received, though unworthy of it; but it did not much benefit him: for issuing, by the handiwork of Satan, from his grave at night-time, and pursued by a pack of dogs with horrible barkings, he wandered through the courts and around the houses while all men made fast their doors, and did not dare to go abroad on any errand whatever from the beginning of the night until the sunrise, for fear of meeting and being beaten black and blue by this vagrant monster. But those precautions were of no avail; for the atmosphere, poisoned by the vagaries of this foul carcass, filled every house with disease and death by its pestiferous breath.

Already did the town, which but a short time ago was populous, appear almost deserted; while those of its inhabitants who had escaped destruction migrated to other parts of the country, lest they too should die. The man from whose mouth I heard these things, sorrowing over this desolation of his parish, applied himself to summon a meeting of wise and religious men on that sacred day which is called Palm Sunday, in order that they might impart healthful counsel in so great a dilemma, and refresh the spirits of the miserable remnant of the people with consolation, however imperfect. Having delivered a discourse to the inhabitants, after the solemn ceremonies of the holy day had been properly performed, he invited his clerical guests, together with the other persons of honour who were present, to his table. While they were thus banqueting, two young men (brothers), who had lost their father by this plague, mutually encouraging one another, said, "This monster has already destroyed our father, and will speedily destroy us also, unless we take steps to prevent it. Let us, therefore, do some bold action which will at once ensure our own safety and revenge our father's death. There is no one to hinder us; for in the priest's house a feast is in progress, and the whole town is as silent as if deserted. Let us dig up this baneful pest, and burn it with fire."

Thereupon, snatching up a spade of but indifferent sharpness of edge, and hastening to the cemetery, they began to dig; and whilst they were thinking that they would have to dig to a greater depth, they suddenly, before much of the earth had been removed, laid bare the corpse, swollen to an enormous corpulence, with its countenance beyond measure turgid and suffused with blood; while the napkin in which it had been wrapped appeared nearly torn to pieces. The young men, however, spurred on by wrath, feared not, and inflicted a wound

49

upon the senseless carcass, out of which incontinently flowed such a stream of blood, that it might have been taken for a leech filled with the blood of many persons. Then, dragging it beyond the village, they speedily constructed a funeral pile; and upon one of them saying that the pestilential body would not burn unless its heart were torn out, the other laid open its side by repeated blows of the blunted spade, and, thrusting in his hand, dragged out the accursed heart. This being torn piecemeal, and the body now consigned to the flames, it was announced to the guests what was going on, who, running thither, enabled themselves to testify henceforth to the circumstances. When that infernal hell-hound had thus been destroyed, the pestilence which was rife among the people ceased, as if the air, which had been corrupted by the contagious motions of the dreadful corpse, were already purified by the fire which had consumed it.

We now leave the medieval era and move forward in time, as we continue to cast our net wider in search of more English vampires …

MYLOCH AND NESMO

THROUGHOUT THE SUMMER and autumn of 1754, a private green-lacquered horse-drawn carriage prowled the streets of Georgian London after nightfall. Its aristocratic-looking passenger was on the lookout for victims – female victims – young and old, whom he could entice into the coach's plush interior, in order that he could have his wicked way with them. However, his motives were not purely sexual, but involved the drawing off of large quantities of blood from the women, via the veins in their necks. The 'gentleman' would begin his bizarre seduction by gently kissing the women's necks and whispering sweet nothings into their ears. When they had relaxed sufficiently and succumbed to his charms, his true intentions would be made all too obvious. Baring a set of horrible sharp fangs, he would plunge them deep into the tissues of their necks, occasionally piercing the carotid artery – with fatal consequences. The victims of these vampiric attacks, be they alive or dead when our gentleman had finished with them, were either dumped down a dark alleyway, or thrown into the Thames like so much rubbish.

A haemophiliac is someone who has a blood-clotting deficiency which can be very injurious to their health. A haematophiliac, on the other hand, is a person with a fetish for drinking blood. The haematophiliac who was carrying out these outrageous attacks was rumoured to be an obscure Count by the name of Myloch, who had arrived in London from Gratz in Styria (now a province of Austria). The reports of the aristocrat had died down by early December of that year, and most rational-minded people in the capital and elsewhere dismissed the stories of blood-drained female corpses as far-fetched tales unworthy of serious attention. Yet others were deeply troubled and worried that Count Myloch had merely left London to satisfy his blood-craving in the villages and hamlets of England's countryside.

A man who claimed to be an expert in Satanism believed that Count Myloch was associated with Sir Francis Dashwood's so-called Hellfire Club, which met in the chalk-mines of West Wycombe. Members of this dastardly club allegedly indulged in obscene sexual orgies, Devil-worship, hedonism of all kinds, alcohol and drug abuse, as well as other indecent and illegal activities.

Almost a hundred years after the rumours of the Georgian vampire Myloch had faded into folklore, the name Myloch unexpectedly resurfaced in an isolated vampire report in Sussex, in the summer of 1851. John Morton, a farm labourer at Pulborough, claimed that his sweetheart, fifteen-year-old Jane Hubbard, had fought off a strange-looking attacker who had entered her bedroom in the middle of the night. She had awoken at about 1 o'clock in the morning to find a bald yellow-faced man with red eyes and pointed teeth leaning over her, inches from her face. As the intruder lunged towards her in an attempt to bite her neck, the plucky teenager slapped his face, grabbed a hefty silver candlestick from her bedside table, and began to club the back of his head as she screamed for help. The girl's uncle, a muscular blacksmith by the name of Joseph, soon dashed into the room and tried to tackle the weird-looking assailant, but he was too quick for him. He jumped out of the open first-floor window and landed like a cat in the street below. Jane Hubbard and her uncle watched from the window as he ran off at an unearthly speed.

The fiend was seen hurtling past the village church by a Mrs Townsend, the local greengrocer, who had been unable to sleep that night and had got up to make herself a cup of hot milk. She had been idly staring out of the window at the quiet street when she had seen the figure charging past. She couldn't fail to recognise him, because he was the same man who had recently broken into her house and attacked her in her own bedroom. He had attempted to rape her and the attack had made her very nervous and afraid of the dark. She called out to two men meandering down the street on the way back from a long drinking session at the village inn. They did their best to apprehend the villain but they had both drunk too many tankards of the local brew to be any match for his incredible speed and agility.

The mystery deepened when a traveller from Crowborough arrived at a lodging house in Pulborough in the August of that year. John Wakefield, was a renowned storyteller and, in addition, he also claimed to be a necromancer, an exorcist, a demonologist, a healer and a hunter of vampires. Furthermore, he warned the other guests at the lodgings that Count Myloch, who had been at large in London and the Home Counties a century before, was on the prowl again in Sussex, and that they had better watch out.

When Wakefield heard about the ochre-skinned ghoul, described so vividly by Jane Hubbard and Mrs Townsend, he set out to hunt him down, convinced he was none other than Count Myloch, up to his old tricks again. Using an obscure form of divination involving a device in a box that resembled a magnetic compass, he roamed an ancient deer park on the slopes of the South Downs, until he came upon an isolated cottage, which proved to be the lair of the vampire. However, the crafty bloodsucker was far too quick for Wakefield, and fled away, his cloak billowing out behind him. However, the vampire hunter had managed to catch a glimpse of the Austrian parasite's face – the very same face that he had seen a year before looking through his sister's bedroom window at their home in Crowborough. On that occasion, Wakefield had fired a pistol directly at Myloch, but he had melted back into the darkness, seemingly unscathed.

Wakefield pursued Myloch across the country as far as Kent, but the fugitive vampire managed to evade capture once more, disappearing without trace just as they approached Gravesend. Wakefield later claimed that Count Myloch had returned to his old prowling ground in London and had moved into a palatial old house in company with another vampire – a Polish immigrant with the surname Nesmo, who had committed suicide in 1823.

In the early nineteenth century, all kinds of taboos surrounded the burial of those who had committed suicide, and elaborate superstitious precautions were undertaken to prevent the deceased person from returning back to life as a vampire. In Nesmo's case he was buried face-downwards at a crossroads near Hamsptead Heath, with a wooden stake driven through his mid-section. This necessary but distasteful practice was carried out on the stroke of midnight, on a piece of unhallowed ground which is now bisected by Spaniards Road.

Weeks after the burial, a ghastly-looking figure was seen walking like a somnambulist away from the crossroads one night, and Nesmo's grave was later found to be empty. Bodysnatchers, who had perhaps unearthed the corpse to sell to a medical school, were immediately suspected, but others put a more sinister twist on the disappearance, fearing that Nesmo had risen from his grave as a vampire.

Strangely enough, in the 1920s, there was a gruesome but intriguing report about a group of children who would often pay a visit to the 'vampire's house' – the nickname they had given to a crumbling old mansion on the Belsize estate, within a stone's throw of Spaniards Road. The children were fascinated by the creepy house, which was the subject of many childish dares.

One day, twelve-year-old Susan Browne was challenged by her peers to put her hand through the front-door letterbox of the mansion, and to keep it there for a count of ten. Terrified, but not wanting to be called a coward, she put on a brave face, lifted the corroded brass flap and gingerly inserted her hand into the slot. No sooner had she done so, than she began to scream and scream and scream, before quickly snatching her hand back out of the letterbox. Moments later, she collapsed on the steps, with blood spurting from her hand. Two of her fingers were missing – bitten clean off at the knuckles.

The police were called and made a forced entry into the house but as far as they could see, no one had lived there for several years. They could not find the child's missing fingers anywhere in the building. There was also no evidence of any recent squatters in the building, because the place was festooned with cobwebs, which showed no sign of any recent disturbance.

Someone, or something, was responsible for biting off that child's fingers ... Could it be possible that it was Count Myloch, up to his dastardly old tricks again?

Dorset Vampires

The Monmouth Ash

DORSET IS THE HOME of the headless phantom of the Duke of Monmouth, or so the ghost-hunters and folklorists tell us. The so-called Monmouth Ash Tree, standing between the villages of Woodlands and Horton, is reputed to mark the spot where the Duke was captured after his escape from the swamps of Sedgemoor, in July 1685, and the grisly phantom of the long-dead Duke has been spotted in the locality, minus his head. The Duke met a gruesome end in the Tower of London as a punishment for his rebellion. The crowd of bloodthirsty onlookers had winced as they watched the executioner's axe make several attempts to chop off his head completely. The Monmouth Ash, under which the Duke was apprehended, became a shrine to him after his death, with many of his friends and admirers visiting the tree over the years to carve their initials into its knarled trunk.

The family of the woman who betrayed the Duke was despised and cursed. She herself was said to have been afflicted with an horrific wasting disease, and other members of her family had died from mysterious illnesses within months of one another. The cottage which the family had inhabited collapsed not long after these uncanny deaths, and a strange tall man in black was seen to prowl about the ruins after dark. The general consensus was that the figure was a vampire.

A vagrant who had sought refuge in the ruins of the cottage awakened one morning to find blood pouring from a gaping neck wound of unknown origin, that refused to clot for hours. Days later, a young lady passing the cottage to rendezvous with her secret lover was viciously attacked and had her neck and breasts bitten all over by a tall dark stranger in a flowing cloak. When she screamed out for help he vanished without a trace.

Travellers forced to pass by the cottage ruins always made sure they wore talismans and gypsy charms to protect themselves from the entity, whose nefarious activities seemed to peak on nights when there was a full moon. The face of the alleged vampire was chalk-white, his eyes deep red, and his breath was described as being 'plague-ridden'. In every one of the reports, he is described as wearing a long cape, similar to the 'opera' cloaks which were commonly worn at that time by the wealthy.

Doggett – the Vampire of Tarrant Gunville

Seven miles north-east of the Monmouth Ash, lies the sleepy little village of Tarrant Gunville, situated at the head of the Tarrant Valley, close to the mysterious Neolithic earthwork known as the Dorset Cursus, which runs over six miles across the chalk downland of Cranborne Chase. To the east of Tarrant Gunville stands the surviving west pavilion of the stately Georgian residence, Eastbury House, built by George Doddington, Lord of the Admiralty, in the early eighteenth century. Doddington died in 1720 with Eastbury House still unfinished. He bequeathed the incomplete mansion, along with thirty-thousand pounds – a fortune at the time – to the corpulent dandy George Bubb.

In the last year of Bubb's life, he became the Baron Melcombe of Melcombe Regis, when King George III granted him a peerage. The cost of running such a large rambling mansion as Eastbury House was prohibitive for the two people who inherited the property after his death in 1762. Richard, Earl Temple, was the first of these, followed by George, second Earl Temple, who was prepared to offer anyone two hundred pounds per annum if they would live at Eastbury House and look after the place, but he found no takers.

In the end, since Earl Temple had retired to his retreat in Italy for health reasons, his loyal steward, William Doggett, found himself burdened with the responsibility of dealing with the white elephant property. Acting in what he imagined to be his master's best interests, he took the decision to demolish the south wing of the house. After the demolition, he sold the rare and expensive salvaged building materials with the intention of ploughing the money back into the rest of the building, which was badly in need of repair. Unfortunately, his good intentions were never realised and all the money found its way into his own pockets.

When Lord Temple returned from Italy and found what Doggett had done in his absence, without any consultation, he was angry and disappointed and made his feelings quite plain to his steward. Doggett, consumed with guilt and shame for what he had done, felt he had no alternative but to take his own life. So that night, he shot himself through the head inside the house, dying instantly. The pool of blood which formed around his head soaked through the carpet and the floorboards, creating a stain which proved impossible to remove.

Surprisingly, for the times, permission was granted for Doggett's body to be buried in the consecrated ground of Tarrant Gunville churchyard. In those days, the Church usually insisted upon all suicide victims being buried in unconsecrated ground, as the act of suicide was considered a mortal sin. A crossroads site would most often be chosen and a stake would be hammered through the corpse's mid-section, to prevent it from rising again and terrorising the living.

Even though he had been spared the ignominy of such an unholy burial, William Doggett did not rest in peace under the sanctified soil of that churchyard, but instead rose up and 'walked' once more to torment the living. Just three days after his funeral, he reappeared as a vampiric predator, wearing a long dark violet coat, a wig, and knee breeches tied with his distinctive yellow silk ribbon. Those unfortunate enough to encounter him at close quarters, testified that his eyes were lifeless and sunk back into his skull, and that his mouth formed a downturned crescent from which long pointed teeth protruded. He prowled about near the gates of Eastbury House for several nights, and was later seen peering into the windows of his former home.

A group of poachers on the estate was allegedly attacked by him one moonless night; the attack leaving one of them seriously wounded, with a deep bite wound to his forearm, which soon began to fester and turn gangrenous. The unfortunate poacher was discovered a few days later, lying doubled up in a ditch under a hedgerow. The poor fellow was delerious and foamed at the mouth as his body was wracked by violent convulsions, which eventually killed him. Because of the circumstances surrounding his death, the poacher's ravaged body was burned by his friends in a clearing of a local wood, to prevent him from returning to life as one of the 'undead'.

Blood-Sucking Ghoul

One day, some months later, a young thatcher from the nearby village of Witchampton was fooling around on the roof of a cottage which he was supposed to be thatching, when tragedy struck. He lost his balance and toppled off the roof, breaking his neck and killing him instantly. In order that his friends and neighbours could pay their respects, a wake was held at his home and his body was placed in a polished elm coffin, which was left open in the front room. In the middle of the night, strange noises were heard coming from that room, which woke the boy's father. He crept downstairs to investigate and in that moonlit parlour he could plainly see a ghastly-looking man bent over the coffin and sucking at the neck of his dead son, making revolting slurping noises. The boy's father could scarcely believe the evidence of his own eyes and ears. His son was now sitting bolt upright in the coffin, staring straight ahead with blank white eyes – the pupils were no longer visible – whilst the creature feasted on his blood.

He was confused and horrified, and went to fetch a sword that he kept upstairs at his bedside. When he returned, the blood-sucking ghoul had vanished, and his son was lying peacefully in his coffin once again. It was only when daylight began to creep into the room the next morning that the two deep puncture marks on his throat were discovered – marks which filled his father with dread.

The lad was duly buried several days later, but his solid-looking ghost was seen on many occasions after that, often stalking two local girls whom he had known when he was alive. Fear and anxiety swept through the local community – something had to be done to stop these hauntings, but what? and who would undertake the task?

And so it was that a Catholic priest was brought to the churchyard and was soon standing at the graveside of the young thatcher's troubled spirit. The boy's body was exhumed to enable it to be exorcised and thus be rid of the evil spirit that had turned it into a vampire. When the corpse was examined, fresh blood was found on the lips, and the face did not bear the usual grey pallor of death, but instead had a rosy complexion, with no trace of decay. Sliding the eyelids back, the priest noted that the eyeballs were blood-red and flecked with gold.

An exorcism was performed with the utmost haste – even the priest, armed with his holy water, was reluctant to spend any more time than was strictly necessary with this unnatural corpse. He muttered the prayers and incantations as quickly as he could and before the coffin lid was replaced, a rosary was strung around the neck of the corpse, as an extra precaution.

Hasty or not, the exorcism did the trick, for after that, the thatcher's apparition was seen no more, but the vampire Doggett remained at large for many years, until his body too was exhumed in the year 1845. His body also bore not a trace of decomposition, but looked pink and fresh and in the best of health. Some say that Doggett's flew eyes open as the daylight fell upon them, and were etched with a look of terror before a vampire hunter hammered a hawthorn stake through his heart, finally ending his reign of terror.

Very Rough Justice

Decades before Doggett was born, another vampire is said to have stalked the Dorset countryside, but information on this bloodsucker is very scant. Sometime in the seventeenth century, two drunken robbers of Evershot decided to attack an old man who was thought to be carrying a bag of gold coins. The robbers laid in wait and ambushed the elderly man as he returned late at night from an inn. They searched him roughly and soon found the gold. Not content with their precious haul, they then sadistically beat him up before inflicting a crippling blow to the back of his head with a large stone.

The old man was found at the roadside shortly afterwards, groaning and semi-conscious as his brains spilled out from his skull like the yolk from a lightly boiled egg. People never recover from such an attack and the poor man died soon afterwards, and his killers were subsequently brought to justice after a landlord heard them laughing and joking about their sadistic act in the bar of his tavern one night.

The two murderers were fastened alive into iron cages, similar to the gibbets in which hanged men used to be displayed. The cages were chained to either side of an ancient oak tree, dangling from two massive branches. And there the murderers were left to die of thirst, starvation and exposure to the inclement weather. The doomed duo begged for food and drink from passers by, but even the most sympathetic person who heard their cries dared not help them, or he or she would be severely punished by the law. Their refusals were met with the most vitriolic strings of abuse. One of the men grew so desperate that he bit into his own hand and arm to consume his own flesh and wet his parched throat with his own blood.

Within days, the miscreants became so weak and despondent, that they had given up all hope and waited for death. Their pleading and cursing had stopped and they stared with glazed eyes at those who came to gloat at their final agonies. A heavy shower of rain roused the starving men and quenched their thirst for a short while, but when night fell, they shivered in their soaked clothes, their misery now complete.

One night, as the lives of the two murderers slowly ebbed away in their dangling cages, something terrifying and other-worldly took place near that oak tree. The shadowy figure of a man approached in the moonlight and stopped directly beneath the cages. He wore a flowing cape and as he looked up, the two men could see that his face was paler than death. He began to focus his attention on one of the caged killers, then suddenly lifted himself off the ground and effortlessly flew up to the cage, as if he were a bird. He reached his hand between the bars of the cage and pulled out the man's emaciated arm. As the weakened man looked helplessly on, he bit deep into his wrist and wrenched off a piece of withered flesh.

A night watchman had witnessed the whole thing and heard the howl of pain as the muscles and tendons of the wrist were severed by the stranger's sharp fangs. He hared off to the village to raise the alarm, for he knew at once that the flying caped man was no ordinary human but was most probably the vampire who had been on the prowl for many years in the area.

By the time the watchman and several of his companions had returned to the tree, they found one of the cages swinging in the wind, empty. The murderer who had had his arm bitten off by the vampire had somehow managed to make his escape. The bars of the cage had been wrenched apart as if they were matchsticks. The other caged killer died that night as he was being quizzed over his partner in crime's incredible escape.

That same night, the landlord of the inn who had been responsible for the killers' detection and arrest was attacked in his bed by an intruder who tore the flesh from his face with his clawed hands. The landlord was also bitten on the neck and arms as he tried to defend himself from the frenzied fiend. He fought back at his assailant, swinging an iron poker at him that he kept under his bed for just such an emergency. The poker hit home and the assault ceased. The landlord was astonished to see the intruder fleeing to the open bedroom window and diving suicidally into the street, some twenty feet below. Incredibly, he seemed to suffer no harm when he landed on the cobbled road, but ran off at a phenomenal speed and was soon lost to sight.

The attack left the landlord a changed man. His health declined, and he began to suffer from strange hallucinations and incessant palpitations of the heart, which made sleeping impossible. He couldn't eat or drink and barely spoke to his family and friends. His life had been reduced to such misery that he decided to end it all. He took a knife and plunged it through his heart, and death quickly followed.

The two vampires remained at large in that area of Dorset, creating pain and distress whenever they felt the urge to leave their lairs and seek out new victims. Some think they are still around today, along with many others of their kind who have been turned into vampires over the centuries.

Subterranean Vampires

Keep Well Away from Brandon Colliery!

TWO AND A HALF MILES south-west of Durham, lie the rusting remains of the disused Brandon Colliery. The colliery spewed out coal, day and night, for over a century. Having been first opened in 1856, to produce coal to help fuel the Industrial Revolution, the last miners hung up their pit boots in 1968. There is an eerie silence about the place today and few people venture on to the site, littered as it is with huge pieces of rusting machinery, whose purpose has long been forgotten. Weeds and saplings have already begun to sprout up everywhere, camouflaging the mine workings, and in another hundred years all traces of the mine will probably be lost.

Like many a coal-mine, Brandon Colliery has seen its fair share of tragedy. Its underground tunnels and shafts have been the scene of a large number of accidents and cave-ins, fatal and otherwise. Many of those who lost their lives in the bowels of the mine were only children, such as pick-carrier Frank Love, who, on 31 October 1871, died tragically, aged just twelve years.

One summer evening in 1969, a woman from Meadowfield, a small village in County Durham, ran up to a policeman as he pounded his beat, in a very distressed state. She gave the constable a chilling account of a man in black who had attacked her as she was making her way home. He had wrestled her to the floor, and then attempted to bite her neck. Fortunately, the approach of a gang of children had startled him and the assailant had leapt to his feet and run off at an incredible speed. Helping the woman to her feet, the children told her that they had seen the same weird-looking man a few days previously, running down the grassy embankment leading on to the railway tracks of Brandon Colliery Station. Not only that, the father of one of the children had also seen the sinister man in his outdated black costume coming from the direction of Brandon Colliery a fortnight before that and had warned the children to keep well away from the place.

Rumours spread like wild fire around Meadowfield and beyond, that a vampire was at large in the vicinity of the abandoned coal-pit. Several people came forward claiming to have had encounters with the vampire, and quite a few of these reports described a red rash around the creature's mouth and a pair of long fanged incisors. The flurry of reports continued until the autumn, when the nights around Brandon Colliery were once again filled with an uneasy silence, broken only by the faint creaks and groans from the depths of the mine, as pit props rotted and gave way and tunnels collapsed.

Was it all just hysteria, or could it be that one of the undead miners had somehow managed to extricate himself from the crushing earth which had buried him and risen again to stalk the people of his own village, Meadowfield?

There have been other reports of vampiristic entities prowling in the inky voids of caverns and quarries and disused coal and limestone pits around Britain. What better place for a vampire to have his or her lair, than in the secluded pitch-black depths of a coal mine hundreds of feet below ground?

The Hamstoke Vampire

The Hamstoke Vampire was said to live in just such a setting in the Goonzion Down mines of Bodmin Moor, Cornwall, in the early nineteenth century. Little is known about this vampire, beyond the local tales of a shadowy hunched figure that roamed the moor after midnight, often at the time of the full moon, in search of vulnerable late-night travellers making their way along the lonely paths and tracks amongst the heather. Hamstoke, the parish after which the vampire was named, was, with the exception of Alternon, the largest parish in Cornwall. It was bounded by St Cleer, Alternon, Broadoak, Temple, Blisland and Warleggan.

It was on Bodmin Moor, in the vicinity of this latter village, that an alleged vampire attack once took place. Even today, with the advantage of electricity, good roads and modern communications, the place feels isolated and remote and has an atmosphere which would normally deter all but the most fearless inhabitants from taking a midnight stroll across the moor.

Around the year 1800, however, two girls in their teens decided to sneak out of their grandmother's cottage in Warleggan one night to rendezvous with a gypsy boy they had briefly met that day. Elaina Jones and Mary Reddon, who were cousins, foolishly decided to walk for three miles north of Warleggan on to the chilly moor in search of adventure and romance. The weather on Bodmin Moor was, and still is, notoriously fickle; the skies can be clear one minute and obliterated by blizzards the next. There was certainly a chill in the air when the girls set out that night and Elaina held aloft a lantern to light their way, as the sky was moonless and the moor stretched out before them like a jet black carpet.

They had only gone about a mile when the weather suddenly changed for the worse. A strong westerly wind started to blow and quickly extinguished the lantern. Soon torrential rain hammered down on the moor and the girls were quickly drenched to the bone. They became disoriented and as they battled their way through the storm, they wandered far away from the place where they had agreed to meet the gypsy lad.

Out of the darkness a man suddenly appeared and persuaded the girls to accompany him to an old cottage. Hopelessly lost and shivering with cold, they had little choice but to accept his offer, albeit it with deep misgivings. They couldn't see the man's face, but there was something about his gravelly voice which filled them with foreboding. Once inside the cottage, they clung on to one another in front of a roaring fire, trying to dry out their saturated clothes, still unsure of the stranger's motives. He soon asked the girls to remove their clothes so that he could dry them properly, but they politely declined, saying that they preferred to dry their soaked clothes whilst still wearing them, "but thank you all the same, sir".

This angered their strange host and he made a sudden grab at Elaina, and tore off her coat and bodice, but as he tried to bite into her lower neck and shoulder, Mary grabbed a red hot poker from the fire, and after pushing its glowing incandescent tip deep into his back, she clubbed the back of his head, but not as hard as she would have liked, because all her limbs had been weakened with fear. Elaina managed to extricate herself from the loathsome grip of her attacker, as he groaned like an animal from his terrible wounds. She and Mary quickly escaped into an adjacent room and managed to bolt the door. In this room, which served as a kitchen, they almost tripped up on what, at first, they took to be a bundle of rags. They soon realised that it was actually an old woman lying dead on the floor. The foulest imaginable smell was coming from the corpse, making them both retch. They noticed that she had two prominent red puncture marks on her wrinkled neck and they exchanged terrified glances.

The man then began to bang heavily on the door but he said nothing. Elaina and Mary quickly prised open the kitchen window, and having made their escape, darted off into the wild and windy night, desperate to get away from the villain's clutches. They thought they could hear the unearthly attacker crying their names out after them, or was it just the wind howling across the desolate moors? By some miracle, after running aimlessly across the moors for what seemed like half the night, they eventually reached Elaina's home and she and Mary fell down on the doorstep, exhausted, soaked to the bone, and in floods of tears.

After berating them for their illicit nocturnal escapade, Elaina's grandmother told her grand-daughters that they had almost certainly nearly met their grisly fate at the hands of Brucker, the Hamstoke Fiend. He was a vampire, she explained, who was thought to be the offspring of a local trollop named Jane Williamson and the Devil himself. Brucker spent the daylight hours sequestered in some abandoned and waterlogged mines deep under Bodmin Moor. Some people thereabouts also claimed that he was in league with demonic sprite creatures known as Kobolds.

It is thought that the Hamstoke Vampire struck again in the 1900s, when a schoolteacher from Launceston was enjoying a day out picnicking on Bodmin Moor with his sweetheart. The young man was moved to quote Oscar Wilde during a particularly spectacular sunset. Staring into his lover's eyes, he proclaimed: "Death must be so beautiful. To lie in the soft brown earth, with the grasses waving above one's head, and listen to silence. To have no yesterday, and no tomorrow. To forget time, to forgive life, to be at peace!"

Suddenly, a sniggering sound was heard from behind the couple. The schoolteacher turned round, expecting to see some of his more unruly pupils poking fun at his expense. Instead, he was shocked to to be confronted by an abnormally tall thin man dressed from head to toe in black, with an unnaturally pale face and a head devoid of any hair. His eyes were nothing more than thin dark slits and his hands were abnormally large, with long slender fingers that tapered into pointed nails. The teacher quickly helped his fiancée to her feet but as he did so the tall freakish man lunged at them. He clawed at the teacher's face and tore off the arm of his shirt, as the woman ran off screaming down the hill to seek help.

When she returned to the scene of the attack accompanied by a farmer and his son, they found the teacher kneeling in the grass with blood streaming from his now empty eye sockets. In his left hand he was clutching one of his own eyeballs, which had obviously been clawed out by his attacker. His right hand was desperately searching about amongst the grass for his other eyeball. Upon seeing this macabre sight, his sweetheart fainted. The teacher remained kneeling in shock for a while then he also lost consciousness, due to lack of blood and the severity of the pain of his injuries.

When the teacher was later examined by a doctor, odd puncture marks, certainly not made by normal human teeth, were found on his left forearm. The police searched long and hard for the violent culprit but he was never found, and the locals talked in hushed tones about the return of the Hamstoke Vampire in the inns around Warleggan and St Neot. They say that garlic was sold in great quantities that year, and that hawthorn crosses were hung on many a door to repel the dreaded vampire.

Was the attacker merely the teacher's jealous rival, or some madman attacking at random? Or could he have been the (apparently ageless) Hamstoke Vampire?

Unfit to Wear the Dog Collar

There is a curious epilogue to these tales of the Hamstoke bloodsucker. In 1931, a very unpopular and eccentric man of the cloth – the Reverend Densham – took on one of the most troubled incumbencies on record, at

St Bartholomew's Church in Warleggan – at the age of sixty-one. Within a very short time, Densham had alienated his congregation to such an extent with his idiosyncratic ministry, that he ended up topping the fence of his rectory with barbed-wire and allowing Alsatian dogs to roam the grounds. The doors of St Bartholomew's were opened to only a select few with whom Densham saw eye to eye, and if these chosen few parishioners were just so much as a minute late for one of his services, they would find the church doors bolted against them. A majority of the local people forming the small congregation were farmers, yet Densham frowned on their carnivorous eating habits and declared that vegetarianism was the only civilised way to eat.

In the end, the congregation dwindled and dwindled until just two brave souls still attended Densham's services, and then he even managed to insult these final loyal churchgoers. A close friend pleaded with the harsh Rector to be less strict with his flock but he remained unrepentant of his Draconian methods, and remarked of the villagers of Warleggan: "They all come to me in the end, as I conduct all the funerals. They won't come to church on their feet but they have to come in their black carriages."

Incredibly, the deranged Reverend continued preaching to his non-existent congregation and eventually even resorted to placing life-size cardboard cut-outs of worshippers in the pews! What's more, after each pointless service he would record in the parish register: 'No fog, no wind, no rain, no congregation'. The Reverend Densham refused to visit his flock in Warleggan, either in sickness or in health, nevertheless, in the 1950s, when rumours circulated about the local vampiric fiend being active once again, several people wrote to Densham to tell him about the strange sightings of the ghoul. They need not have bothered; he had already had first-hand experience of the fiend. A shopkeeper in the village who delivered milk and food to the barmy Rector learned from him that the apparition had recently visited St Bartholomew's Church during one of Densham's sermons to his cardboard congregation, and the visitation had given him a very nasty turn.

Not long afterwards, the Reverend Densham was found dead on the staircase at the rectory, with a look of intense terror etched on his twisted face. The locals put forward all kinds of theories to explain his strange demise, the most popular of which was that the 'thing' had visited him and scared him to death. Despite Densham's wishes to be buried within a specially created garden of remembrance in the grounds of the rectory, his body was instead cremated and the ashes sprinkled at a public park of remembrance in Plymouth. The villagers of Warleggan were not in the mood to grant the wishes of someone who had shown them so little respect in life and no doubt did not want to be reminded about that crazy period in their church's history.

Incidentally, a similar series of events, albeit with a less sinister outcome, were unveiled during a rare ecclesiastical court sitting in London, in the summer of 2007, in which a senior Church of England vicar was accused of "being a bully and a liar" and of spitting at one of his church wardens. The sixty-year-old vicar in question, the Reverend Thomas Andrews, of St Mary and St Michael Church in the sleepy backwater of Trumpington, near Cambridge, since 1999, was brought before the court when he was accused of bringing the "once thriving" parish to breaking point. He managed to alienate virtually everyone connected to his church, it was alleged, from the once-loyal volunteer flower arrangers and cleaners, to his church wardens.

The tribunal was also told that The Reverend Andrews chose to ignore the advice of the parochial church council. Giving evidence, Justin Gau, representing the council, said, "This is a very sad case – it is in fact an old-fashioned divorce caused by irretrievable breakdown between a priest and his parish. Dr Ambrose is a square peg in a round hole. He has talent, he is intelligent and learned, but he is also a bully and a liar. He would lose his temper if he did not get his own way, and he was incapable of [accepting] the beliefs of others, if they did not fit his own. He brought a thriving parish to its knees."

During the court sitting, he was also accused of sending hate e-mails, telling members of the congregation who opposed him to leave – just like the Reverend Densham – and even of making personal attacks from the pulpit on those with whom he did not see eye to eye.

It is a sad day when those appointed to be our moral and spiritual leaders let us down in such a spectacular fashion.

Mystery of the White Scar Caves

Beneath the looming mass of Ingleborough, one of the magnificent 'three peaks' in the Yorkshire Dales National Park, there exists a labyrinthine network of underground caves, providing vistas below ground which are no less spectacular than those above. The caves were first discovered in 1923 by two amateur geologists, Long and Churchill. The 'White Scar Caves', as this network is now called, encompasses one of the largest cave chambers in Britain, and they are now open to the public as a popular tourist attraction.

Throughout the 1930s, there were sightings of an enormous dark-blue bat-like bird which flew to and from the White Scar Caves, mostly during the twilight hours. This strange unidentified creature was thought by some of the locals to be a vampire bat. The bird's wingspan was estimated to be some six feet or more, and the head of the ominous 'cryptid' (as cryptozoologists term such unknown species) had very distinctive pointed ears.

In 1933, a man by the name of John Bray was so fascinated by the idea of an unknown species living in Yorkshire, that he kept a series of vigils in the caves, desperate to catch a glimpse of this sinister bird of the night. His long uncomfortable watches throughout one particular cold winter's night eventually paid off, when the giant bat finally put in an appearance. John Bray stifled a gasp of astonishment as the huge creature landed in the mouth of the cave. He immediately noted that it had all the characteristics of a human being, only with the addition of a pair of huge wings. However, he only saw the creature in silhouette in the cave mouth, against the backdrop of a moonlit sky, dotted with scudding snow clouds. The apparently human-bird hybrid was startled when it detected Bray's presence and emitting a blood-curdling shriek, it flapped its great wings, and then flew back out of the cave at an incredible speed.

John Bray's curiosity was even further aroused by what he saw that night and he held successive vigils, hoping that the bizarre creature would return, so that he could study it more closely. But he was to be disappointed. Perhaps his presence had frightened the strange creature off. Whatever the reason, it never returned and he eventually had to give up his quest.

Many other people claimed to have seen this 'birdman' on its nightly excursions, including a policeman from the village of Chapel-le-Dale.

Is it a Bird? Is it a Bat?

A similar giant bird with human features was reported between September 1968 and June 1970, mostly at sites located along the Bridgewater Canal at Preston Brook, as well as in parts of Runcorn, in Cheshire.

At around 11pm one night, in September 1968, two men sitting on the deck of a barge on the canal at Preston Brook, watched in disbelief as an enormous dark bird, with a wingspan of at least twelve feet, descended from a clear and starry sky. It landed with a mighty thud on the roof of another barge which was moored about sixty feet away from them in the marina. The men were so terrified by the sight of the giant bird, that they rushed for cover inside their canal boat. There they cowered, not daring to go back up on deck until they had heard the creature's wings flapping, as it took off again.

The same over-sized bird was seen during the following month over east Runcorn and Murdishaw, and several witnesses described the flying monstrosity as resembling a giant bat.

These unidentified overgrown birds have been seen across the globe, and many theories have been expounded in an attempt to explain their existence. Some argue that they are pterosaurs, a type of prehistoric bird which may not have completely died out millions of years ago when the other dinosaurs met their mysterious worldwide death, as had been supposed, but had managed to survive in isolated pockets in different locations. Others are convinced that the creatures are merely an, as yet, unidentified species of bird. On the surface, this may seem rather unlikely, and most ornithologists would scoff at the possibility. Yet the coelacanth is a species of prehistoric fish which was thought to have been extinct since the Cretaceous Period (145 to 65 million years ago), until a large specimen of the fish was caught off the east coast of South Africa in 1938, and others have been caught since.

So is it really possible that a bird, universally believed to have been extinct for millions of years, could still be flying around today? It is highly unlikely, if only because of the sheer size of the creatures, so what are we to make of these giant bat sightings? Could they perhaps be visitors from some parallel universe, or could the answer lie in the supernatural sphere? Is it possible that these monstrous creatures of the wing could be vampiric beings, which have undergone some sinister metamorphosis to become bat-like humanoids?

*

In the spring of 1922, an enormous black bat, with a wingspan of six feet, was spotted circling the spire of West Drayton Church during the night of a full moon. Several terrified witnesses watched the creature suddenly dive down into the churchyard, where it hopped about among the gravestones as large as life. When it was chased by two policemen, the creature let out a deafening bone-chilling screech, which sent all the spectators diving for cover. It then flapped its massive wings, and clearing the gravestones, soared skywards.

An old man who claimed to have seen the same giant bat twenty-five years previously, maintained that it was the spirit of a vampire who had murdered a woman in order to drink her blood in Harmondsworth, in the 1890s.

*

In Thornton Heath, in Surrey, in 1938, a woman reported being attacked in her bedroom in the middle of the night on three separate occasions by a large winged creature with a fanged mouth. On each occasion it flew into her bedroom like a whirlwind and then drew blood from her neck with its sharp fangs. The poor woman's nerves were shredded by the attacks, which left her weak with fear.

*

One night, in November 1963, four teenagers were walking along a country road near Hythe in Kent, laughing and chatting away happily, when they saw something which stopped them dead in their tracks. As they clung on to each other in fear and trembling, the tall figure of a man, dressed from head to foot in black, but minus its head and with 'bat wings' sprouting from its back, approached them on foot. As the headless apparition drew nearer, the terrified teenagers turned on their heels and dashed off in fright.

Their description of this entity is remarkably similar to that of the so-called 'Mothman' which haunted parts of the state of West Virginia in the United States, in 1966. Like the Kent entity, Mothman did not seem to have a head in the normal sense of the word, but instead had two luminous red eyes set into its chest. From its shoulders there sprouted a pair of featherless wings, which were described as being like those of a bat. Many people testified to having seen the creature, and to this day, the truth about Mothman remains a mystery.

*

The 'Cornish Owlman' – a humanoid entity with wings and large red owl-like eyes – was sighted in Cornwall between 1976 and 1978, and although the encounters with the creature were widely reported in the press, the authorities refused to take them seriously and didn't even bother to investigate any of them.

We all undergo metamorphoses, or bodily changes, day by day, as part of the ageing process, but the concept of shape-shifting in vampires predates Bram Stoker's fictional *Dracula* changing into a bat. Vampires were not only thought to be able to take the form of a bat, but also the forms of many other animals, including dogs and wolves, through a type of 'transfiguration'. The most famous example of transfiguration is the one that took place when the face of Jesus became as radiant as the sun and his robes became as white as snow upon Mount Thabor. This transformation, referred to as 'metemorphothe' by St Matthew and St Mark, has allegedly also been observed in several mediums throughout history.

Queenie Nixon, a Northampton-born medium, gave many a demonstration of an astonishing form of physical metamorphosis from the 1950s to the 1980s. During these demonstrations, her face would change into that of a total stranger. Sitters at Queenie's spell-binding performances would first become aware of a gaseous substance, similar to cigarette smoke, that would begin to swirl around her face. This would be followed by the gradual materialisation of pale 'masks' on Queenie Nixon's face, which, within minutes would become that of a girl, or an old man, sometimes even sporting a moustache or a beard.

This phenomenon is usually explained by mediums in terms of ectoplasm and trance states, but scientists are sceptical of such claims. Could the vampire be capable of such metamorphosis, in which he or she turns into a bat-like creature? It certainly provides food for thought ...

Cloaked Stranger at the Coal-Face

Most of Lancashire is undermined by a honeycomb of coal-pits, and many of them, thanks to Margaret Thatcher, are now disused. It is said that in the Wigan area, many of these disused collieries are haunted. Considering the loss of life that was common down the coal mines in the nineteenth and twentieth centuries, this is not surprising, but one particular 'haunting' is of special interest, because it involved the apparition of the archetypal Dracula type of vampire. The case was reported by a Preston journalist, William Topping, around 1919, and was also investigated by a trio of amateur vampire hunters. These three brave real-life Van Helsings were: Jonathan Carmichael, a bookseller from Workington, Cumberland; John Warwick, a photographer from Carlisle; and a soldier named James Dunne, who hailed from Bolton.

In 1897, at an unnamed colliery near Wigan, miners, upon reaching the bottom of the mine, used to have to walk for almost half an hour, often bent double and with only the light from the lamps on their helmets to guide them, in order to reach the coal face.

One evening there was a commotion at the colliery because a very strange-looking man had been seen prowling about the workings at a considerable depth. It can be extremely hot and humid at the bottom of a mine and many miners are forced to wear next to nothing during their shifts. So it is easy to imagine how someone dressed in a suit of dark velvet and a long opera cloak would stick out like a sore thumb at the coal-face. This out-of-place individual was reputed to be over six feet in height, to have black slicked-back hair, and a haughty, aristocratic face. On his long slim fingers he wore a dazzling collection of gold and silver rings encrusted with a variety of larger-than-life gemstones.

The strange character displayed the unnerving habit of literally appearing out of thin air at various locations underground. On one occasion he even made the long ascent from the pit bottom in the cage, along with two terrified miners who had just finished their shift. During the journey to the surface he addressed them in a foreign language – possibly French – and as soon as he strode out into the night air he turned into a huge bat and flew off into the ink-black sky. The weird foreigner was seen five times in all, and on the last occasion the vampire hunters Carmichael, Warwick and Dunne, who had heard about the strange shape-shifting nobleman from the relative of a miner at the pit, decided that it was time for a showdown.

They arrived at the colliery uninvited but they were soon given permission by the supervisor to track down the suspected bloodsucker, who was making the workforce very nervous and therefore affecting production. The cloaked stranger was soon spotted sneaking about in one of the darkest recesses of the mine by a collier who raised the alarm. The vampire hunters soon gave chase, but unfortunately the intrepid threesome were forced back when their quarry retreated down an old disused tunnel which they were told was deemed unsafe because of a number of recent cave-ins. That tunnel extended for a quarter of a mile underground, eventually connecting to yet another pit, where the oddly-dressed foreigner soon made his presence felt when he started haunting those workings. His nefarious activities only ceased when part of the mine caved in whilst he was inside it.

A body was eventually recovered from the tangle of rock, coal and crushed pit props. However, the corpse was not that of the suspected vampire, but of a young miner.

Dark Forces Beneath Billinge

What must rate as one of the most bizarre examples of underground vampires was said to have been encountered on numerous occasions in the tunnels under Billinge, a small town which lies about five miles south-west of Wigan. This area is dominated by a hill – known locally as the 'Lump' – the crown of which looks down from six hundred feet above sea level on to sixteen counties. It is also possible to see Ireland, Scotland, the Welsh Hills, as well as other areas of Britain and beyond from this breathtaking vantage point, but there are lesser-known places of interest beneath the bedrock around Billinge, and a case in point is the unidentified church that was swallowed up into the earth at some time in the distant past.

One afternoon, in the late eighteenth century, four local children, growing tired of play, went looking for adventure. They decided to go and explore the limestone caverns that dotted the area, despite the dire warnings of their parents. The children did not return for their evening meal, nor the whole of that night, nor the next, nor the next. They had simply vanished. Extensive searches of the caves revealed nothing at all; not a scrap of clothing, nor a dropped toy. Then, just when everyone had given up all hope of ever seeing any of them again, one of the children, nine-year-old Will, eventually resurfaced and revealed the terrifying and gruesome fate that had befallen his three friends.

He told how they had not been long in the caves, each clutching the stump of a candle, which they had brought from home, when a group of old men with long beards and black and green velvet clothes had suddenly appeared and grabbed hold of them, pinning their arms behind their backs. Seconds later, one of the men had started biting into the neck of the youngest child, a boy of five. His terrible screams had echoed through the caverns, whose walls had amplified them still further, terrifying the other children, who all started screaming in unison.

Amidst all the noise and confusion, Will seized the opportunity to escape and he ran off as fast as his legs would carry him, desperately trying to remember which way they had come in. He was pursued by three of the bizarrely-dressed old men, their lanterns casting grotesque dancing shadows on the cave walls. Somehow he had managed to outrun them all. At one point, Will stumbled over a pile of what seemed to be human bones in the middle of a torch-lit chamber, and the discovery frightened him so much, that he looked frantically around for an escape route. Just then he noticed a tiny dot of light in a far corner of the chamber and he rushed towards it. Daylight! The hole was extremely narrow but he managed to squeeze through it, the circle of blue sky beckoning him upwards.

He had almost made it out of the cave, when a cold hand grabbed hold of his ankle and began to pull him back down into the cave. Will kicked violently with both feet, hitting his assailant directly in the face. His foot was soon released and he popped out of the cave wall like a cork from a bottle. Without so much as a backward glance, he sped off home, yelling for help as he did so.

The case was deeply worrying in its own right but the authorities were also concerned because a number of other people had recently gone missing from the area close to the cave entrances. Two heavily armed soldiers (possibly Dragoons) descended deep into the caverns, each carrying a torch, on the lookout for anything suspicious. When they resurfaced, looking pale and fearful, they claimed that they had not only found Will's heap of human bones, but also the ruins of an ancient church of some unknown denomination. The church had fallen into decay in a great vaulted chamber, but it had not been totally abandoned. No indeed! The interior of the church was lit by three large candles, illuminating a series of grotesque gargoyles which formed part of the altar and casting eerie dancing shadows on the cave walls.

Without waiting to find out who, or what, might have lit those candles, or for what purpose, the pair started racing back to the exit as if their lives depended on it. Throughout their underground explorations, the two soldier said they felt as if they were being watched, and they also heard whispered voices speaking in an unknown tongue.

One report even said that a severed child's head had been found in one of the caves, as well as several large stone jugs full to the brim with congealed human blood. These discoveries were both taken to be evidence of cannibalism and the local community angrily demanded protection from whatever dark forces had taken up residence in their caves. This time the authorities did take things seriously and a large quantity of gunpowder was used to seal the cave entrances and the disappearances abruptly stopped. Nevertheless, it still left the riddle of the underground church of Billinge unresolved. How had it come to be there? and who was responsible for the lighted candles which the soldiers had found?

*

Sunken churches are to be found not only in Lancashire, but in many other corners of the British Isles. In Lincolnshire, for example, you will hear the legend of the sunken church of Sancliff, in which the whole church and its congregation of habitual sinners, was said to have been swallowed up by the earth during morning service.

Then there is the legend of Kirkstanton Chapel, which also reputedly sank into the ground along with its priest and all its worshippers one fateful Sunday morning. Some modern folklorists believe that an earthquake was to blame for the 'sinking' of the church but the truth of the matter has never been established.

At Fisherty Brow, near Kirkby Lonsdale, a legend has been told for centuries about yet another church that vanished into the ground along with its parson and his congregation. From time to time, phantom bells have been heard at the spot where the church slid down into the clay, and many people, upon visiting the spot and putting an ear to the ground, have claimed to have heard the faint ringing of church bells.

The Fifth Duke of Portland

Vampires are reputed to detest the daylight and particularly bright sunlight, and I sometimes wonder if some of the nineteenth century's great eccentrics were, in fact, vampiric beings.

Take the reclusive Fifth Duke of Portland, William John Cavendish Bentinck Scott (1800-1879), for example. The Duke had an extensive subterranean complex excavated under his estate at Welbeck Abbey in

North Nottinghamshire. The network included eight tunnels, covering a distance of fifteen miles in total; an underground ballroom occupying ten-thousand square feet and capable of accommodating two thousand dancers; a billiards room for twelve full-size billiards tables; and even an underground library. Do not imagine that the rooms in this labyrinth were dark and gloomy. Not a bit of it! They were lit by hundreds of gas-jets and painted in a specific shade of pink chosen by the Duke, which unlikely colour was the only one agreeable to his eyes.

The Duke was renowned for his outright hatred of sunlight, his favourite time of day being from sunset to sunrise. In fact, so fond was he of sunset, in particular, as it signalled the beginning of his 'day', that he had a dramatic sunset scene painted on the ceiling of his huge ballroom. If unavoidable circumstances forced him to travel during the day, the Duke would make his journeys inside a specially-designed black hearse-like carriage with shuttered windows, thus ensuring that no daylight could reach his skin.

This aversion to daylight was not the Duke's only foible; he also hated social interaction. So much so that direct verbal communication with people outside his immediate circle was strictly forbidden, something which all his staff were acutely aware of. Even when he was taken ill, the doctor was not allowed into the Duke's chamber to see him, but instead had to instruct the valet to take his lordship's pulse and conduct the examination of his patient from behind a door.

Rumours naturally abounded concerning the mysterious fifth Duke of Portland; some said that his face must be badly disfigured, or that he must have a gruesome-looking skin disease, but a rare photograph which he had had taken of himself during the time of his self-imposed isolation, showed him to be a perfectly ordinary, if rather pallid, man with bushy side-whiskers and dark shrewd-looking eyes. The photograph showed no obvious deformity of any kind; certainly no reason to hide himself away from the world. Still the rumours concerning him flew about – there obviously must be wild orgies going on in his underground lair, for why else would a reclusive lonely man want a ballroom for two thousand dancers? Other people decided that he had made some kind of pact with the Devil, for what other reason could make him shun daylight and only walk in the grounds of Welbeck

Abbey in the dead of night? And what of the Duke's bizarre taste in food? His extremely limited diet was reputed to consist of nothing more than a freshly killed chicken every day.

In 1879 the Duke died and he was buried at Kensal Green Cemetery in North London. Not long after the burial, strange whisperings began to circulate about the deceased nobleman, to the effect that he had been leading a double life at Welbeck Abbey. Apparently, this rumour had its origins in the extraordinary claims made by a widow of Baker Street, London; a woman by the name of Anna Maria Druce.

Mrs Druce asserted that the late Duke had been none other than her husband, Thomas Charles Druce, owner of a popular store called the Baker Street Bazaar. Thomas Druce was supposed to have died in 1864 but Mrs Druce claimed that the burial had been completely bogus, and that the coffin had actually been filled with lead. This fake burial had supposedly been staged by the Duke because he had grown tired of his alter ego, Thomas Druce, and he wanted to return to his reclusive life at Welbeck Abbey.

Anna Druce's claims must have been taken seriously because Thomas Druce's grave in Highgate Cemetery was reopened, and the coffin removed for inspection. It was not found to contain lead at all, but merely the bearded decomposing corpse of Mr Druce. This discovery caused the case brought to court by the scheming Mrs Druce, to collapse. That was not the end of the matter though, because for several months after the fifth Duke of Portland was laid to 'rest', his ghost was seen prowling around Kensal Green Cemetery, wearing a long black cloak and a dark green velvet suit. Was this apparition merely the phantom of the Duke? Or was the man who went out of his way to avoid daylight during his lifetime really a vampire? More may be revealed about this fascinating and elusive character one day.

HAMPSHIRE VAMPIRE

The Strange Tale of Jack Savage

THERE ARE MANY SUPERSTITIONS surrounding the death of a person. At the moment of death, for example, tradition in many places across Britain dictates that doors and windows should be opened, and that mirrors should be covered over in case the spirit of the deceased should enter one of them by mistake. Nowadays, it is usual for a dead body to lie in a chapel of rest until the day of the funeral but in the past, wakes were traditionally held in the deceased person's house, and the body would lie in its coffin so that all the person's friends and relatives could come and pay their last respects. Indeed, such traditions still continue in some parts of the United Kingdom to the present day. Superstition dictates that a corpse at such a wake must never be left alone, or in the dark, lest it become the prey of demons, and from this custom we derive the ritual of the wake – which is in essence a vigil to be kept on a body.

There is also a now even rarer custom regarding the passage of the soul of the dead person to the world beyond, which is known as 'sin eating'. This somewhat unhygienic ritual involves sprinkling salt on to the chest of the dead person and leaving it there for a while until a plate of six or seven newly-baked savoury-tasting cakes have been placed on a specially prepared table draped with a black tablecloth. This tablecloth is sometimes embellished with a skull and crossbones.

Pinches of salt are then picked from the chest of the corpse and sprinkled on to these cakes, which are then consumed by the mourners partaking in the sin eating ritual. By consuming the cakes sprinkled with the salt in this way, the partakers believe that they are actually eating the sins of the deceased, and thus cleansing the body of all wrongdoing in preparation for the afterlife.

This ritual was carried out on the corpse of an old Hampshire farmer by the name of Jack Savage, who died some time in the early nineteenth century, probably in 1810. The story regarding the alleged resurrection of this farmer was related to a Hampshire folklorist in Victorian times by one Alfred Summers, the landlord of the White Swan inn in Winchester, in 1899. The tale was also corroborated by several other people, who had in turn heard the 'yarn' from their elders.

After his death, from what seems to have been a stroke, Jack Savage was laid out in his coffin on the kitchen table at his cottage near the ancient Forest of Bere, and the sin eating cake ritual commenced. For some obscure reason, never properly explained by the storyteller, the body of Farmer Savage was not permitted to be buried in a Christian churchyard, and so it was interred instead in a secluded spot in the nearby Forest of Bere.

A fortnight after the burial, two soldiers hired by a local farmer to catch poachers on his land, were patrolling the periphery of the Forest of Bere one night around midnight, when they caught five gypsies in the act of carrying out a bizarre ritual at the side of Savage's unhallowed grave. They had dug up Savage's coffin, bound it in three chains, and then attached a small crucifix to the coffin-lid. The oldest of the gypsies defended their actions by explaining to the soldiers that the man in the coffin had been rising from his grave at night to attack people in the area, and had bitten his little grand-daughter, a girl of eight years of age. As a result of the attack the child was now delirious and being cared for back at the gypsy encampment by a man called Jonathan, who was renowned for his immense knowledge of vampires.

The soldiers had known Jack Savage personally and were sickened to find his coffin being abused in such an irreverent way. In any case, they were very sceptical about the old Romany's unlikely tale, and they ordered him and the other gypsies to remove the chains from the coffin and to rebury it immediately. With great reluctance, the gypsies slowly unbound the coffin, removed the crucifix from its lid and lowered the earthly remains of Jack Savage back into the ground. They then headed back to their camp deep inside Bere Forest without exchanging another word with the soldiers, but inwardly seething with resentment.

Three days later, in the dead of night, the two soldiers were again patrolling the farmstead near Bere Forest, when they glimpsed a terrifying sight by the pale light of the moon. A tall thin bony man was darting back and forth amongst a clump of trees with the speed and agility of a spider. The figure was moved so quickly and jerkily, that the soldiers' eyes were barely able to follow it, but at one point, when the eerie man kept still for a few seconds, an opening in the low clouds allowed sufficient moonlight to reveal that the swift prowler was none other than the dead farmer, Jack Savage. As the military men squinted through the trees in the silvery moonshine in horrified disbelief, the ghastly-looking apparition of Farmer Savage flitted towards them. One of the soldiers managed to rapidly draw his flintlock, take aim and fire, but he missed his target by a mile because the ghoul was zig-zagging wildly as he approached. The other soldier then drew his pistol and calmly took aim and fired. There followed a bright flash and the accompanying bang, as the metal ball flew at the head of the weird-looking attacker from beyond the grave.

The seemingly carnate, solid, flesh-and-blood ghost of Jack Savage stopped in its tracks and clutched its left eye with its hand, as blood streamed down its face. The projectile from the flintlock had destroyed the resurrected man's left eye, leaving a bloody, jagged-edged socket where his eye had once been. In a pain-induced fury he lunged at the soldier who had harmed him – a man named Ned – and proceeded to bite into his neck with such ferocity, that the flesh was torn wide open and hung down in shreds and arterial blood spurted high into the air from the severed vein.

The second soldier did not hang around to see what the ghastly phantom's next move would be. Instead, self-preservation set in. He deserted his wounded comrade without a second thought and dashed to his employee's farmhouse in abject panic, hammering on the door to be let in.

In one version of the story, the body of the soldier Ned was never found, but according to another narrative, his contorted body was discovered some time later underneath a hedge, completely drained of blood and with his back snapped in two, so that the back of his head touched his buttocks. After this shocking discovery, a rumour quickly spread that Jack Savage had risen from his unhallowed grave as a vampire. In an attempt to quell such ungodly rumours, the vicar from

82

the nearby market town of Fareham lectured his congregation from the pulpit, saying that there were no such creatures as vampires; it was all a lot of superstitious nonsense.

However, a lay-preacher in the town knew better, and rejected the vicar's dismissive attitude, for he himself had had dealings with numerous people in England and France over the years who had been troubled by vampires. The vicar scathingly replied that it was impossible for a man to rise from his grave, but the lay-preacher was adamant. He defended his claims by quoting the accounts documented in the Bible about various resurrections: Ezekiel's vision of the valley of dry bones being restored as a living army of flesh and blood; the resurrections performed by Jesus, such as the raising from the dead of the daughter of Jairus; the reanimation of a man in the middle of his own funeral; the recalling of Lazarus from his tomb; and of course, the resurrection of Christ himself and the account of the dead saints who came out of their tombs to enter Jerusalem after Jesus had risen from his own tomb. After Jesus, the Bible also mentions a resurrection of a female named Tabitha by Peter.

Curiosity seekers from all over southern Hampshire converged on Bere Forest, hoping to catch a glimpse of the so-called vampire, and some were not to be disappointed. A bailiff from Winchester by the name of Knapp, and a local physician named Benwell, encountered the vampire during a vigil on the south-western fringes of Bere Forest at around two o'clock in the morning. They had been sitting around a fire for some time, discussing the nature of the supposed bloodsucker, and speculating about the reasons Savage might have had for returning as a vampire. Jack Savage had been something of an enigma whilst he was alive. He had lived as a semi-recluse – an outcast from the rest of society and there were those in the community who believed that he had led a debauched life. Some who had known him in life believed that because he had been shunned by most people during his life, he had returned as an outcast from the realm of death.

Knapp and Benwell talked on this subject well into the night, until their fire was nothing more than a small pile of glowing embers. They had just agreed that they should probably turn in, as it looked as if they would see nothing that night, when they heard a small sound behind them. "Probably just an animal nosing through the undergrowth," said Benwell, but when they turned to look in the direction of the sound, they were startled to see the wild-eyed subject of their conversation emerging from the cover of Bere Forest and standing less than two hundred feet away from them, gazing at the dying embers for a full minute or so as if mesmerised.

Knapp cocked his flintlock, ready to fire should the vampire attack, and Benwell dipped a dry branch into the fire to use as a torch, intending to confront the freakish-looking creature. However, as soon as the two men got to their feet, the vampire slid silently back into the forest. Knapp was not at all keen to go along with Benwell's suggestion of tracking the creature back to its lair. Anything could happen in the forest. It could be lying in wait for them at this very moment. The bailiff eventually persuaded the doctor to give up the pursuit of the vampire that night and the two men set off for home, all eyes and ears, in case the creature should ambush them on the way.

On the following evening, shortly after sunset, Jane Hutton, a seven-year-old blind girl, heard someone come into her bedroom late at night. She called out to ask who was there and received no reply. Then a coarse hand started stroking her face and patting her head, and the foul breath and body odour of the silent intruder reeked of rancid meat. Jane started to whimper and then to cry out loudly. Her grandmother, hearing her cries rushed up to her little room under the eaves of the thatched cottage, to see what was the matter. She found the window flung wide open and the child sitting up in bed in abject terror. The rotten stench of the mysterious interloper still hung in the air, and the grandmother, remembering the tales of the vampire of Bere Forest, slammed the window shut, and plucked little Jane from her own bed and placed her safely between her parents.

The mysterious goings-on had put the whole community on edge, yet no one knew how to tackle such an elusive and dangerous foe. Eventually the vampire expert, Jonathan – whom the gypsies had mentioned to the soldiers guarding the farmer's land – was sought out and consulted. He was described as a man of around fifty years of age, of middle height, with long sandy-grey hair, lantern-jawed, and an excellent swordsman. A traveller from Southampton by the name of Keel described the vampire specialist as a man of military bearing, who had served in the Anglo-Turkish War, despite his relatively advanced age.

The enigmatic fellow himself would provide the locals with no details of his background, beyond documented proof that he was born in Northumberland in 1760. A few paranoid villagers believed he was a French spy, but most of them recognised that the man was an honest authority on the Occult, and on vampires in particular, and welcomed his intervention. The people living around the perimeter of Bere Forest clubbed together and were able to offer a small reward to Jonathan, in return for permanently laying the vampire of Jack Savage to rest. He politely declined the prize money and reassured them that he would find and destroy the fiend for them anyway; he sought no reward.

Around this time, the young gypsy girl whom Savage had attacked made a complete recovery, thanks to a herbal medicine formulated by the intriguing and courageous vampire hunter. This inspired confidence in the man even further and many men and women of all ages volunteered to be of assistance to him. But the vampire-killer refused all offers of help and instructed everyone to stay indoors on the designated night when he would hunt down the parasitic fiend and eradicate it forever, so that not a trace of the creature remained.

Jonathan made an inspection of Jack Savage's grave by the light of day and found the coffin empty, which proved to him that he had another lair somewhere else. By some supernatural means, which may have involved dowsing, the vampire hunter traced his sinister quarry to an ancient hollow tree where the unholy leech could be heard faintly snoring away the daylight hours. Jonathan hammered an iron spike straight through the trunk so that it emerged on the other side, and the vampire let out a bloodcurdling high-pitched scream, because the spike had reached its target and pierced its heart. The huntsman of the undead then tore away the canopy of intertwining leaves and creepers from the side of the trunk where the creature had entered and left its arboreal sanctuary, thus allowing the sunlight to shine directly on to the right side of the writhing vampire, instantly vaporising the flesh from half of its face and its right hand. The vampire's left eye had been shot out by one of the soldiers guarding the farmstead some time before, and the remaining eye turned red and began to bleed profusely because of the exposure to ultraviolet light from what the creature regarded as this accursed adversary.

To finish off what he had begun, the vampire hunter then hurled a bucket of highly inflammable liquid, which was said to be 'Greek Fire', on to the trapped and impaled creature. Greek Fire, once a closely-guarded secret of the chemists of Constantinople, cannot be extinguished with water, which instead, only serves to intensify the flames, and so when it began to rain, the fire flared up and not only burnt the vampire to destruction, but also consumed the entire dead hollow tree, until all that remained was a pile of embers.

By dawn, the local people saw nothing but charred bones among the smoking embers of the tree, and these skeletal remains of the vampire were systematically destroyed in a blacksmith's furnace, until they too were turned to powder. The vampire of Jack Savage never prowled southern Hampshire again and soon afterwards, Jonathan, the mystifying vampire hunter, left the area with a convoy of gypsy caravans and was heard of no more.

Rumours of a Royal Vampire

The Secret of Glamis Castle

THE GRIM AND FORBIDDING hulk of Glamis Castle stands in the great Vale of Strathmore, in Tayside, in the north-east corner of Scotland. For centuries, the vast fortified castle, with its pointed towers, has held a sinister reputation for housing an unspeakable and terrible secret, but just what is the nature of this dreadful secret? It is said that only certain members of today's British Royal Family know the secret, but there have been whispers and deeply unsettling rumours circulating about the dark mysteries of Glamis Castle for hundreds of years, and these strange claims are the subject of the following accounts.

One thing has been definitely been established, and that is that the Glamis Secret has nothing to do with a stubborn bloodstain that has proved to be impossible to remove from the floorboards in one of the castle's rooms. That stubborn stain is known to be the blood of King Malcolm II, who was cut down by the Claymore swords of his rebellious subjects inside the castle in the year 1084; nor is the secret anything to do with the fact that Lady Glamis was burnt at the stake outside the castle for practising witchcraft, although it is true that her ghost still walks the corridors and is known as the Grey Lady. No, the secret of Glamis Castle lies in solving the grotesque and baffling jigsaw puzzle of weird events which I am about to relate.

If you were to stand outside the castle and count the number of windows, and then compare them with the number of windows inside the building, the totals would not tally – you would always find yourself to be two windows short. In other words, there seems to be a walled-up secret room in Glamis, and what this room contains has been the subject of much debate and speculation for over six hundred years. No one knows where this secret room is, but some say it is on the top floor of the castle, inside one of the towers.

Then there is another clue – over the centuries, a succession of servants has claimed to have heard resounding thuds on the walls of the building. What is more, one of the Earls of Strathmore said that he once overheard King James V mentioning 'the thing' locked up in its room. Many servants at the time speculated that this thing was a deformed overgrown child; the product, perhaps, of the continual inbreeding over the centuries within the aristocracy. Some researchers believe this might just be the case, for in one of the castle's oil paintings, a strange green-clad figure of a child can be seen and he has an obviously deformed torso. The identity of the painting's subject has never been established.

Nearly all castles have been the scene of horrific events at some time in their history, and so it is with Glamis. In the year 1486, a particularly nasty event occurred there when a party of neighbouring aristocrats, the Ogilvies arrived en masse at Glamis, begging for protection from their sworn enemies, the Lindsay family, who were out to get them. If they had expected a warm welcome and neighbourly charity inside the castle walls, they must have been bitterly disappointed. Far from being invited into the castle and given the protection they sought, they were escorted without further ado into a dark and airless chamber in the bowels of the castle and abandoned there without food or water for over a month.

When the chamber was finally reopened, the stench inside was appalling, as no provision had been made for any sanitation and it was no surprise that only one of the Ogilvies was still alive. This poor man was in the most shocking physical condition and he could barely stand. The fetid atmosphere inside the room was unbearable and the gaolers' torches threw light on a scene of unimaginable horror. Driven by starvation, the survivor had been driven to eat from the corpses of the members of his own family and their incomplete remains littered the filthy floor of the room.

This sadistic streak in the family showed itself again in the seventeenth century, when an unfortunate black slave was said to have been stripped naked, turned loose and then hunted as 'fun game' by the Earls and their hunting dogs. The slave was repeatedly impaled with lances and the dogs allowed to literally rip him apart while the ladies of the castle looked on, laughing and chatting as if they were watching a game of croquet. The murdered slave's ghost is very probably that of the strange figure known as Jack the Runner, who has been spotted darting about the castle's rooms and corridors screaming in agony.

Around the time that this slave was hunted to death, a young woman from the local village who had unwisely become romantically involved with one of the Earls, was said to have accidentally stumbled upon the secret chamber in Glamis, after one of her trysts with her lover. Whatever she saw must have been utterly chilling, because she ran screaming from the castle as if her life depended on it.

The poor girl was later captured by two Royal henchmen and taken to the castle's dungeons. One of the henchmen then took a pair of iron tongs and brutally ripped out the young girl's tongue and threw it on to the fire. This barbaric practice was known as the 'Ritual of Silencing', and had also been performed on several servants over the years, when they had inadvertently stumbled upon the Glamis Secret. The shock of having the tongue wrenched out at the root more often than not killed the victim instantly. If it did not, they usually bled to death anyway, but the poor innocent young maiden in this case, ran out of the castle dungeon, minus her tongue, in a state of utter terror with blood gushing out of her mouth. The henchmen gave chase and soon caught up with her. One of them grabbed her in a headlock like a vice, then twisted her head round until her neck broke. The body was then meticulously sawn up into small chunks, like so much meat, and fed to the wild boars in the forest.

The unmentionable secret of Glamis was briefly touched upon in 1904 when the thirteenth Earl of Strathmore, Claude Bowes-Lyon, told an inquisitive friend, "If you could only know the nature of the terrible secret, you would go down on your knees and thank God it were not yours." The Earl's cryptic remark only deepened the mystery, but the friend he spoke to later claimed that he had found the secret chamber. In order to silence him he was quickly bundled off to the colonies; some say he was sent to Australia.

Early in the twentieth century, when the daughter of the fourteenth Earl of Glamis repeatedly pestered her father to let her into the family secret, he told her, "You cannot be told, my dear; for no woman can ever know the secret of Glamis Castle."

It is claimed that certain members of the current Royal Family know of the terrible secret, but they are all male. Apparently, they are traditionally told on their eighteenth birthday, but none of the Royals has ever commented on, or denied, the secret of Glamis Castle.

Curiously, a female vampire has allegedly been sighted flitting about the grounds of the castle from time to time, and legend has it that she is there visiting her child, a half-human, half-vampire, or 'dhampir', as such hybrids are called.

In 1885, George Blizard, an enthusiastic collector of literature on historical oddities, wrote to private investigator John Meikeljohn at his office in York Buildings, Adelphi, London. In the letter, Blizard wrote that he was prepared to offer Meikeljohn a very substantial amount of money, if he could uncover the so-called Glamis Secret. Meikeljohn declined, recognising the fact that the Royals were a powerful family, who could destroy his career and perhaps even imprison him if he delved too enthusiastically into their secrets. Undeterred, Blizard sat down in the study of his Bloomsbury home and wrote to another private detective named Collinson, of Savoy Street, but he also turned down the collector's offer, probably for very similar reasons.

Finally, when word of Blizard's generous offer was mentioned at a gentleman's club, two adventurers by the name of Edward Rye and John Grimstone, took up the dangerous and controversial challenge. Their first move was to apply for employment at Glamis Castle, but only one of them – Edward Rye – was accepted as a junior butler. John Grimstone found lodgings at a cottage several miles from the castle, and the two men communicated by sending Morse Code messages to one another. Grimstone sent his messages by covering and uncovering a bull's eye lantern, and his colleague would reply by doing the same with a candle at one of the windows of Glamis Castle after dark. The two would meet whenever the opportunity arose, usually when Mr Rye was sent to the local village to order in groceries for the castle's extensive kitchens.

According to Rye, in the relatively short time that he had been employed at the castle, he had met two members of staff – a footman and a young female servant – who had both talked enthusiastically and at length about the Glamis Secret. Both their stories mentioned a vampire that inhabited a secret room in one of the turrets. This vampire had come into being as a result of some curse on the bloodline of the Earls of Strathmore, and the creature was allowed to prowl freely about the roof of the castle on most nights. The vampire could not be killed, or harmed in any way, because it had Royal blood in its veins and, even in its present condition, it was regarded as a member of the Earl's family. A quantity of fresh human blood was allegedly taken up to the vampire's secluded lair every few days, but the source of this grisly liquid nourishment remained a mystery.

The young maid went on to tell them how, on one occasion when the Earl of Strathmore and his family were away, the staff had got together and hung towels from every window in the Castle, then went outside to check whether they were all covered. They were surprised to find that there was not one, but several, of the windows where no towel was evident. The girls's voice dropped to a whisper as she gave her opinion that it was because they were the windows of the secret chambers where the Royal vampire was allowed to roam.

John Grimstone corresponded with George Blizard about the extraordinary claims, and the latter sent more money to the two investigators to encourage them to delve a little more deeply into the strange mysteries at Glamis Castle.

Some weeks afterwards, Edward Rye was awakened at almost three o'clock in the morning by an ear-splitting scream; definitely that of a woman, he immediately noted. He stumbled out of bed in his long-johns and cautiously stepped out into the dark corridor outside his room holding a candle. Keeping close to the wall, and making as little noise as possible, he edged his way along the corridor in the direction of the screams. At the end of the corridor he was surprised to find the senior butler standing with his arms outstretched, barring his way.

In the strongest possible terms, the butler advised Rye to return to his bed at once. Nothing was amiss, he said. There was no cause for alarm and he would attend to everything. Rye protested strongly, saying that he had heard a most unearthly scream, which seemed to have come from the upper floors, above his bedroom. It sounded as if someone was being attacked; surely they should both go up and investigate? In a stern voice, the senior servant ordered him back to his room immediately, or there would be serious consequences in the morning. Not wishing to blow his cover, or lose his job, and therefore any chance of solving the mystery, Rye was forced to comply and trundled back along the corridor, burning with curiosity and itching to make his way to the upper floors and confront whatever might be up there.

After that night, the young maid who had told Edward Rye about the vampire that had taken up residence in the castle, was curiously absent, and all enquiries about her whereabouts were met with blank stares. Rye was very worried about his little informant, fearing that it may have been her screams he heard in the night. There was no way he could just pretend that nothing had happened; those screams were terrible. If she was in trouble, he must go and try to help her.

So the following night, well after the household had turned in for the night, Rye left his bedroom to go in search of her. He checked that the coast was clear and then crept into the corridor, this time without a candle and in his bare feet, so as to make as little noise as possible. His heart was in his mouth as he surreptitiously attempted to gain access to the secret chambers in one of the castle's turrets by climbing up a narrow winding staircase, which, of course, was out of bounds to all members of staff. But the senior butler must guessed that he would be unable to let the matter rest and had instructed one of the other servants to lie in wait for him. Rye was caught in the act and roughly bundled back down the staircase. He was brought before the head butler, and sacked on the spot as a nuisance and a trouble-maker.

A despondent Rye and Grimstone therefore had no choice but to abandon their mission and return to London none the wiser. They refused to take any more money from Mr Blizard, feeling they had not accomplished what they had set out to do.

Could there really be any truth in the story of a Royal vampire? Well, even a cursory look into the ancestry of the Royal family throws up some pretty colourful individuals. For example, Queen Mary, the consort of George V, was related to Vlad the Impaler, a barbaric Transylvanian ruler who once killed more than a hundred thousand Turkish soldiers by having them impaled on long spiked wooden poles, as he languidly dipped his bread in their blood at an open-air banquet overlooking the scene of mass carnage. The psychopathic Transylvanian was known as Dracula, Romanian for 'Son of the Devil', and he is thought to have been a major inspiration for Bram Stoker's famous vampire novel, *Dracula*.

Prince Charles then, is the indisputable direct descendant of Vlad Dracula, and in November 1998, when he visited Transylvania during a tour of Eastern Europe, he actually told the newspaper and television reporters covering his trip that he was aware of his infamous Transylvanian ancestor.

The Freedom of Information Act of 2000, was an Act of Parliament that introduced a public 'right to know' – but only in relation to public bodies; it could not be applied to secrets within the British monarchy. The macabre secret of Glamis Castle will therefore remain a closed book for many years to come.

In the Midst of Death
They Are in Life

Intruder in the Grave

A VAMPIRE MAY EXIST as a dead body which continues to paradoxically 'live' in its grave until night-time, when it crawls forth out of its temporary resting place to go in search of blood and 'prana' – the very life-force essence of a human being – to provide it with the sustenance it must have to survive.

Many years ago, in Lancashire, the father of a family died and the family members made arrangements for him to be buried in the family plot in the local cemetery, where a place had been reserved for him alongside three other family members. However, when the grave was opened it was found to contain four other coffins. The man's sons were baffled, because there should only have been three other coffins in the grave, and their father's would have been the last to be buried. The sons assumed that the fourth coffin had been interred by mistake, as it certainly did not belong to any member of their family.

With the help of one of the gravediggers, one of the sons indignantly prised open the uninvited coffin's lid, to try and identify the intruder. He was amazed to find that it came away very easily. It was not even fastened down with screws, as is the usual practice. Inside the sturdy satin-lined coffin there rested a rosy-cheeked stranger, dressed in expensive-looking clothes of the finest velvet and silk. On his fingers he wore a collection of dazzling rings, and the dead man's face was described as having 'a distinctly aristocratic profile'.

The burial would have to be postponed until the riddle of the surplus coffin had been resolved. The frustrated sons, however, were not prepared to leave matters to take their slow bureaucratic course and took matters into their own hands. They entered the cemetery after dark equipped with shovels and spades, determined to oust the intruder from the family grave and so to make room for their dead father's coffin.

This time when they opened the unidentified coffin, they were shocked to find it completely empty of everything but its satin lining, which still bore the imprint of its recent occupant. The brothers did not know what to make of this latest twist in the macabre tale. All they wanted to do was bury their father. Was that too much to ask when the family had paid good money for the communal grave? However, they soon started to realise that there was more to the matter than immediately met the eye. They found out that there had been a recent report of the strange 'vaporous' ghost of a distinguished-looking man haunting the cemetery by night. Could the two things be connected in some way?

A local priest was consulted. He believed the apparition to be that of a vampire who had been seen floating over the gravestones late in the grey foggy November afternoons a fortnight before. Gravediggers had also told the priest about some strange tunnels that they had come across in the same burial ground and of coffins which had been moved, and of disturbed corpses – all indications of the existence of a vampire lair somewhere underneath the cemetery.

There have been many well-documented cases of moving coffins and other baffling subterranean mysteries concerning graveyards. These have been printed in newspapers across the globe, and there is a strong possibility that many of these unquiet graves are also the result of vampire activity. Here are just a few accounts of corpses that have been busy after death.

The Buxhoewden Vault

Situated in the icy expanses of the Baltic Sea, stands the bleak rocky island of Oesel. The island is best known for the whisky it exports around the world, but during the nineteenth century, the island became the talk of Europe for much less mundane reasons: the sinister saga of the unquiet graves …

Upon the island of Oesel, on 22 June 1844, Mrs Dalmann, the wife of a tailor, was driving a horse and cart – which was also carrying her two children – up the long and lonely lane which ran parallel to the town's cemetery. Mrs Dalmann was on her way to visit her mother's grave, as she did faithfully every month. The cart trundled slowly past the many small chapels adjoining the cemetery, which had been built by the island's wealthier families. She finally came to a halt in front of the Buxhoewden family chapel, where she climbed down and hitched the horse to a post. She then walked solemnly into the cemetery with her two children, clutching a bouquet of flowers, and ready to pay her quiet respects to her much missed mother at the graveside.

A quarter of an hour later, Mrs Dalmann and her children returned to the cart to find their horse rearing up and whinnying continuously. The animal was lathered in perspiration and had almost uprooted the post to which it had been tethered. Mrs Dalmann tried her utmost to calm the horse down, but the animal reared up on its hind legs, ears back and the whites of its eyes showing, as if terrorised by something, although there was nothing obvious that could have frightened him. The horse just would not calm down and when all else had failed, Mrs Dalmann was forced to call out a veterinarian to treat her normally placid animal. He bled the horse on the spot – a common practice in those days, which was used to remedy almost anything. The horse finally settled down, and the vet suggested that it had perhaps been stung by a wasp or a bee.

On the following Sunday, the same phenomenon happened again, this time to three horses simultaneously. All three horses had been tied to posts outside the Buxhoewden Chapel and were found quivering with fear and acting strangely when their owners came out to mount them. The same explanation was offered by the vet who had treated Mrs Dalmann's horse: insect stings.

However, on the very spot where the four horses had taken fright, a number of villagers began to hear heavy rumbling sounds emanating from the Buxhoewden family vault beneath the chapel. Over the next few days, the strange subterranean disturbances continued to be heard, and eerie rumours about the unquiet graves of Buxhoewden chapel began to circulate through the town. The tittle tattle finally reached the ears of the Buxhoewden household, via the servants, but it was dismissed as the slanderous invention of some enemy of the family.

However, the gossip about the supernatural goings-on in the vault refused to die down. In the end the Buxhoewdens had no choice but to inform the authorities. They arranged for them to witness the reopening of the vault, in an effort to put an end to the irritating rumours.

When the great granite slabs guarding the entrance to the vault were hauled aside, the investigators found a chilling surprise awaiting them. In the dark and dank interior, all of the coffins had been piled up on top of one another in the centre of the vault. It took three members of the Buxhoewden family, as well as the party of official investigators, half an hour to carry the heavy coffins back to their iron racks, which were mounted around the walls of the vault. No one spoke so much as a word within the vault during this process, because the air seemed charged with an almost tangible atmosphere of dread.

When all of the living had left the underground chamber of the dead, the vault was relocked and molten lead poured over the broken seals of the door, as a precaution against any future tampering. The Buxhoewdens and the group who had accompanied them into the vault, racked their brains to come up with a natural explanation to account for the stacked up coffins, but no such explanation was forthcoming. It was therefore agreed that the incident should be kept secret from the superstitious people of Oesel.

On the third Sunday of that July, eleven horses tethered to posts outside the Buxhoewden chapel became agitated and hysterical during evening Mass. Half of the unfortunate creatures fell frothing to the ground and resisted all attempts by their owners to make them stand. Three of the horses died where they fell, whilst others became so frenzied that they snapped their reins and galloped off in blind panic. Throughout all this commotion, the chapel-goers felt strange throbbing vibrations pounding up through the ground beneath them. The localised tremors were evidently coming from the exact spot where the Buxhoewden family vault was located.

The mystery of the restless dead beneath the chapel could no longer be kept secret or ignored, and the people who had lost their horses, together with a mob of the town's more superstitious inhabitants, joined forces and sent a petition to the Consistory – the supreme governing church body, which periodically held official hearings regarding religious visions and supernatural incidents.

While the tardy white-haired elders of the Consistory considered what action to take over the rumbling vaults, a member of the Buxhoewden clan died. After the funeral, several members of the wealthy family assembled to melt the seals of the now infamous vault and unlock its heavy six-inch reinforced doors. Once more, they found the coffins in a stack in the centre of the vault, and this time there were strange marks on one of the larger coffins, as if it had been battered and chipped at by something. The Buxhoewdens and several brave volunteers repositioned the coffins, including the latest edition, back on to their iron wall racks and then quickly retreated from the vault; no one was in the mood to hang about in the creepy chamber. The locks were changed this time and fresh lead was poured on to the seals surrounding them.

Word got out of this second inexplicable incident, adding more fuel to the creepy rumours of the jumping coffins in the Buxhoewden vault. Now the people of Oesel feared something evil was at large on their island and they made further demands to the sluggish Consistory to take immediate action to protect them. The church court felt under intense pressure to act under this growing criticism, and they opted for a thorough investigation of the haunted vault.

No lesser a person than the President of the Consistory, Baron De Guldenstubbe, consequently went along to the vault with two members of the Buxhoewden family. He duly noted that the doors were locked and their lead seals had not been broken, or tampered with in any way. Another independent witness was summoned and he observed the Baron and the two Buxhoewdens breaking the seals, unlocking the door, then entering the vault carrying lanterns. This witness was also given permission to enter the vault, and when he did so, he came upon a most distressing scene.

This time, the coffins were scattered everywhere in complete disarray, and some of them had been smashed open, partially revealing the decomposed corpses they contained. There was no way that even the most determined grave-robbers could have tunnelled into that vault, which was lined from floor to ceiling with thick slabs of granite. All the slabs were intact, and there was no evidence of any secret openings into the vault. Furthermore, had grave-robbers been responsible for the gross acts of desecration, they would certainly have stolen the expensive diamond rings and other items of jewellery from the bodies.

Replacement coffins were ordered and carried into the vault and the malodorous bodies, in various states of decay, were put into them. When everything had been put back in proper order, someone suggested sprinkling fine wood ashes on the floor of the crypt, so that the ghouls responsible for the grim deeds would leave their footprints behind, should they come again. This ingenious suggestion was enthusiastically taken up, and a fine layer of ash was duly sprinkled all over the vault floor. The mighty doors were then locked and sealed once again.

However, Baron De Guldenstubbe still suspected foul play by person or persons unknown, who were perhaps tunnelling into the chamber in some way. So he employed some workmen to dig a six-foot deep trench around the outside of the vault and posted armed guards day and night at the crypt's entrance.

After a gap of seventy-two hours, the Baron turned up unannounced with two of the Buxhoewdens and once more stormed the troubled vault. Inside, they found that all the coffins were off their wall racks once again, each of them standing on end against the wall. On the floor, there were no footprints in the layer of ash, nor the least sign of any of the coffins having been dragged about. This left the Baron and the Buxhoewdens feeling deeply perplexed – and fearful of the dark forces which were apparently at work in their crypt.

Baron De Guldenstubbe filed his report to the Consistory, and the only suggestion they could come up with regarding the unexplained disturbances, was to bury the Buxhoewden coffins elsewhere. This was duly carried out, and the old family vault was sealed up and abandoned for good.

The mysterious movements of the coffins in the Buxhoewden vault are paralleled in strikingly similar accounts of mobile burial caskets that have been reported in various other countries.

*

According to church records at Stanton, in Suffolk, a burial vault belonging to a French family became the source of loud, unexplained thudding sounds one evening in the mid-eighteenth century.

When the vault was opened for an additional interment in 1755, the large lead-covered burial caskets were found scattered about all over the place. One of the coffins was resting on the fourth step of the stairway leading out of the crypt, and was so heavy, that it took eight men to reposition it on its wooden bier.

Grave-robbers were initially blamed, but the locks on the vault had not been tampered with in any way, and nor had the seals, so the perpetrator of the desecration remained a mystery.

The Mystery of the Creeping Coffins

A similar chain of events was investigated on the island of Barbados in the nineteenth century – the so-called mystery of the 'creeping coffins'. The chilling story dates back to 1724, when the Walronds, a wealthy family of planters, constructed a magnificent blue Devon marble tomb at Christ Church, Barbados. The tomb was the ultimate status symbol, underlining the fact that, although you can't take your riches with you when you go, you can at least be buried surrounded by the sort of opulence you have enjoyed during your lifetime. The locals considered the ostentatious tomb to be more of a fortress than a resting place for the dead, and saw it for exactly what it was, a way of showing off. The floor space, measuring twelve feet in length and almost seven feet in width, was sunk deep into the ground.

Yet, despite such elaborate preparations and financial outlay, for some inexplicable reason, none of the Walronds was ever inhumed in their tomb and so it was eventually taken over by new owners. The first body to be interred there was that of Mrs Thomasina Goddard, on 31 July 1807. Then, in the following year, the vault came into the possession of the wealthy slave-owning family of Thomas Chase, who purchased it in order to entomb two of his daughters, who had died within four years of each other in 1808 and 1812.

When the tomb was reopened in July 1812, for the laying to rest of Dorcas Chase, the coffins containing the Chase daughters were found to to be standing on their heads. Thomas Chase, the head of the family, never recovered from the shock of finding his daughters' coffins standing on end in this way, and he became so mentally disturbed that he committed suicide a month later. And so, on 9 August of that same year, his heavy lead-lined coffin was also placed within the vault by eight pallbearers.

Four years later, on 25 September 1816, the Chase vault was reopened once again to receive the coffin of Samuel Brewster Ames, a little boy who was distantly related to the Chase family. As before, the coffins in the vault were found to be disarranged. Only the burial casket of Mrs Goddard was still in its original place. The other coffins looked as if something had violently thrown them across the vault. There was little the enraged mourners could do but return the coffins to their rightful positions around the walls and then reseal the tomb.

Later that same year, on 17 November, the vault was opened yet again for the interment of Samuel Brewster, whose coffin was being transferred from its original grave in a St Philip churchyard. The sinister reputation of the vault was now so widely known, that large crowds of onlookers had gathered around it in eager anticipation of further developments. They were not to be disappointed, because once more it was discovered that the coffins had been thrown about and this time, the coffin containing Mrs Goddard had not escaped. Indeed, it seemed to have been singled out for special attention, for it had been battered open and her remains exposed.

Searching for a motive, the desecration was initially linked to an abortive slave uprising, which had been severely subdued by the authorities with much bloodshed earlier that year. However, that connection was later ruled out, as there was no way that anybody could have entered the impregnable stronghold of the Chase tomb without using brute force and a large gang of men and such an entry would have left behind a trail of evidence.

On 17 July 1819, the vault was opened for yet another interment and this time the coffin of Thomasina Clarke was taken inside to her final resting place. Outside the crypt, the Viscount Combermere, Governor of Barbados, and two of his officials, waited with bated breath, along with hundreds of hushed spectators. Yet again, the coffins were lying about the tomb as if they had been dropped from a great height and had landed at random. Viscount Combermere was allowed in to inspect the tomb and could put forward no explanation for the mayhem that met his eyes. With his own eyes he had watched the masons struggling to cut free the massive marble slab door of the tomb, as well as the exertion on the faces of the slave gang who had dragged that slab aside. He wondered what kind of force, or entity, could have invaded such an impenetrable crypt and then thrown the heavy coffins about like matchsticks. After the coffins were lugged back to their original positions, a coating of fine-grained sand was sprinkled over the entire floor. This would surely reveal the traces of the mysterious desecrator, the Viscount reasoned. This time, when the vault slab was dragged shut, the Viscount left the impression of his own seal embedded in the cement.

By April of the following year, with no further burials and therefore no reason to open the tomb, burning curiosity had got the better of everybody on the island. They begged the Viscount to sanction the reopening of the Chase tomb, to see if anything had happened in the intervening months. After a protracted debate about the islanders' requests, the Governor of Barbados eventually bent to public pressure, and reluctantly authorised the reopening of the notorious vault.

The seals on the cement were still intact, yet when the interior of the crypt was inspected, the coffins were again found strewn across the vault. Whatever had moved them had done it with such violence, that there were now large dents in the walls of the chamber, caused by the impact of the lead coffins, and yet there were no discernable marks in the sand on the floor of the vault. Viscount Combermere – a fearless man who had been one of the Duke of Wellington's finest cavalry commanders – later admitted that his blood had run cold that day when he came upon the chaos inside the vault. In the end, the Viscount, unable to guarantee the security of the accursed tomb, arranged for the coffins to be removed and buried elsewhere.

The empty tomb was put on the market, but because of its eerie reputation, it was never purchased and still lies empty. Even today, people on the island will not venture near the gaping black mouth of the now open tomb's entrance after dusk.

Something is Stirring in Bebington Cemetery

In the 1950s, a cemetery in Bebington, Wirral, was said to be haunted by an entity that emerged out of holes in the ground between the graves. The outlets of these holes were small enough to be the entrance to a rabbit warren in some places, yet a six-foot-tall man in black was seen to emerge from them, initially as a vapour, which quickly solidified into the form of a man.

The unearthly being was seen initially by an elderly woman who was going to place flowers on her daughter's grave one dusky October afternoon in 1952. This pensioner saw a cone of 'smoke', as she described it, issuing from the ground, and as she looked on, the vapour slowly took on the form of a tall man who stood and stared at her with an expression of pure contempt. His arms were folded in a gesture of defiance, as if warning her not to come any closer, or try to pass by him. The pensioner sensed the threat and turned around and walked quickly away in the opposite direction.

Similar sightings of the same vaporous man in black kept being reported until 1959.

*

Incidentally, there is a grave in this Bebington cemetery which contains the body of a Birkenhead woman who passed away in the early 1960s. The woman – Mrs Emily Filer – died suddenly at the age of sixty-nine from a cerebral haemorrhage. Her thirty-three-year-old son was so distressed at losing his beloved mother, that he attempted to bring her back to life by digging down to her coffin and 'rescuing' her from decay in the realm of the worms. In the mind of this poor man, who was unhinged by utter grief, was the belief that instead of waiting for the mass resurrection of Judgement Day, he could revive his mother and bring her back to health and happiness.

He decided that he would first try and infuse chemical-based energy into the lifeless body by stuffing its mouth with glucose sweets. He then resorted to wiring his mother up to the mains electricity supply in an effort to resuscitate her. Perhaps the muscles of the corpse might have twitched for a while and perhaps reflexive spasms might have rippled through the decrepit limbs, but, of course, the spark of life could not be rekindled. Sometimes it is impossibly hard to let a loved person leave our life, but when death takes them, there is little we can do except hope they are at peace, and if we have sufficient faith, look forward to joining them in the hereafter.

The Frankenstein-like son drew the attention of curious neighbours who grew suspicious as they watched him entering and leaving a certain house that served as his ad hoc laboratory. His facial expressions gave the game away, as the lad looked more and more demented as the days wore on. In the end the authorities were alerted to the situation and they swooped on this grim abode and came upon the exhumed corpse, lying on its unfurled burial shroud with sweets stuffed into its bulging cheeks and wires trailing from the decaying body to the mains outlets. As he was taken into custody, the son was a pathetic figure – grief and desperation having robbed the lad of all reason.

The police were sympathetic to his case and no charges were brought against him. He was clearly more in need of psychiatric help than prosecution. The remains of his dead mother were solemnly re-interred in Bebington Cemetery, where Emily Filer silently awaits that promised day when the dead shall rise from their graves.

If a vampire can cheat death by rising from the grave, could they also survive disasters that no ordinary human could live through? For example, what would happen to a vampire if he or she were to find themselves on a sinking ship at sea?

The following strange story may give us an indication of the resilience of the vampire's physical constitution.

Put on Ice

There are many sane and well-respected people around the world today who intend to have their bodies 'put on ice' when they expire. Their frozen corpses will be stored in liquid nitrogen at a temperature of minus 196 degrees centigrade, until some future time when advances in medical technology will allow the deep-frozen dead to be resurrected. These attempts at cheating death through freezing are practical examples of the relatively young science of applied cryonics. The Cryonics Society of California is a pioneer in this field and started freezing newly-dead bodies in 1967, but there are now cryonic storage societies starting up in other parts of the world.

Many scientists still regard the prospect of cryogenic immortality as a slim and laughable chance, a clutching at straws, because it is still difficult, if not impossible, to freeze human tissue quickly enough to avoid vital-cell destruction. This problem will undoubtedly be resolved in the not too distant future, and already rudimentary human embryos have been successfully frozen at sub-zero temperatures and then gone on to become healthy human beings. Moral watchdogs are concerned at the pace of progress in cryonics, and recent legislation in Britain has limited the period that scientists can hold such embryos in cold storage.

Of course, we don't have to look to cryogenics to find examples of deep-frozen mammals; nature has already beaten us to it. In the summer of 1977, a perfectly-preserved specimen of a six-month-old baby mammoth was disinterred by a bulldozer from permafrost in the Yakutsk Republic of the former USSR. This baby mammoth, nicknamed Dinah, is over ten thousand years old. Even stranger, in 1900, a larger Russian mammoth was found in Berezovka, standing upright in the Arctic permafrost. The frozen beast was so perfectly preserved by the sub-zero temperatures that the ancient buttercups it had been eating moments before it died, were still stuck to its tongue. No reason has ever been given to explain why the mammoth died so suddenly that it never had a chance to swallow the flowers, but the beast seems to have been literally frozen in its tracks.

Human bodies that have been frozen naturally in Arctic conditions have also been reported from time to time. In August 1984, scientists chipped through five feet of gravel and permafrost on Beechley Island, which is situated at the entrance to Canada's Wellington Channel. What the excavating scientists came upon was nothing short of breathtaking – three graves containing the bodies of sailors who had died in 1846. One of the corpses was perfectly preserved. The body was subsequently identified as that of seaman John Torrington, a member of the ill-fated

Franklin Arctic expedition. Sir John Franklin had left England in 1845 on a mission to find the Northwest Passage, a long-sought after sea route leading from the Atlantic to the Pacific, by way of Canada's Arctic islands.

The British Government and its Admiralty were confident that Franklin would find the Passage, and so they provided him with two ice-region ships named *Erebus* and *Terror*, which had been completely overhauled and refitted in preparation for the expedition. Unfortunately, Franklin and his men perished inside the Arctic Circle before they could find the Northwest Passage, but the fate of the two ships was unknown.

However, in 1851, the captain and crew of the brig *Renovation* were astounded to come across two full-sized ships perched on the very top of a towering iceberg in the North Atlantic. Two old seadogs on the *Renovation* immediately identified the ships through a telescope. There was no question about it – they had to be the frozen wrecks of *Erebus* and *Terror*. The nineteenth century ice-bound wrecks were allegedly spotted once more in the early 1950s, still embedded in the icy tomb of the massive iceberg.

There have also been more sinister reports of people frozen in ice. The following story was buzzing across the Internet in the late 1980s and was even reported in a BBC radio bulletin in Britain.

An Icy Grave

According to the story, in March 1988, towards the end of the Cold War, a Russian destroyer was out on manoeuvres in the North Atlantic, about eight hundred miles south of Iceland, when a lookout on the ship spotted an iceberg on the horizon with his high-powered binoculars. The presence of an iceberg was nothing unusual in that area of the ocean in March, but what excited the lookout was the curious dark spot he could see on the iceberg. As the iceberg floated closer to the destroyer, the lookout was able to zoom in on the dark spot, and what he saw made him shake his head in disbelief. The dot was the figure of a woman lying on a small ledge, covered in a thin layer of ice. She was dressed in a black jacket and a long black dress, and was lying on her back.

The captain of the destroyer immediately dispatched a motorboat to take a closer look at the body. Two divers left the boat and swam over to the ledge, convinced that they were going to find the frozen corpse from some sea disaster. Three more men, including a physician, joined them from the ship and spent almost an hour chiselling the body from the ice. The woman, who looked about twenty-five to thirty years old, was perfectly preserved, except for one ankle, which was blackened by tissue-destroying ice crystals. However, the out-dated clothes she wore indicated that she had been frozen for a very long time, perhaps fifty years or more. The corpse was put into a body bag and taken on board the Russian destroyer, where it was put into refrigeration until the ship returned to the Soviet Union.

The corpse was then transferred to a military hospital in Leningrad and gently thawed until it was just under room temperature. The woman's face looked fresh and rosy, presenting the illusion that she was only sleeping, which those present found thoroughly disconcerting. During the examination her eyelids suddenly flew open, startling the scientists standing round. It seemed to be just a reflex action, and not a sign of life, yet, although the blue eyes were slightly bloodshot, they looked animated. All of the scientists present recoiled in shock and watched as the eyes then rolled upwards and the eyelids flickered, and then closed for ever. One report said that the scientists tried unsuccessfully to resuscitate the corpse by firing a high voltage current through its chest, but the lungs were full of ice and the other internal organs were damaged beyond repair. However, there were later reports of the woman being successfully revived.

In the pockets of the woman's coat, several papers and belongings were found, probably snatched in great haste as the ship she was on started sinking. A brooch, a purse with old money that dated to the early 1900s, and a number of documents which confirmed that she had been a passenger on the ill-fated ocean liner *Titanic*, which famously sank after hitting an iceberg 350 miles southeast of Newfoundland in 1912.

It was surmised that the woman had probably fallen or jumped overboard from the stricken vessel, when it became clear that there were not sufficient lifeboats to go round. She had then somehow been swept on to one of the icebergs drifting through the waters, maybe even the iceberg with which the *Titanic* had collided. The story was reported in some Russian satellite states, but the Soviet Union itself allegedly hushed up the strange discovery, because the Russian destroyer that came across the ice-bound corpse had been involved in electronic eavesdropping on very-low-frequency broadcasts from American submarines. The woman had allegedly sailed as a second-class passenger on the *Titanic*, and had originated from London, but the authorities in the USSR provided no further information on this intriguing case.

What else but a vampire could have survived the *Titanic* disaster and remained frozen in ice for over seven decades?

Could a vampire also have been the seemingly indestructible person who survived the following series of maritime disasters?

*

In 1664, a ship sank with eighty-one passengers on board in the Menai Strait which separates Anglesey from the rest of North Wales. There was one survivor: a red-haired man named Hugh Williams.

*

On December 1785, a ship sank with eighty passengers on board, again in the Menai Strait. The only survivor was a red-haired man named Hugh Williams.

*

In the year 1800, a ship sank in the Menai Strait with twenty-five people on board, and all the passengers drowned except for one: a red-haired man named Hugh Williams ...

THE VAMPIRE STALKERS

ON 9 MARCH 1967, a rather unusual message appeared in the personal column of *The Times* newspaper, which read: 'A witch of full powers is urgently sought to lift a seventy-three-year-old curse and help restore the family fortunes of an afflicted nobleman. Employment genuinely offered.'

The afflicted nobleman was the Duke of Leinster, a seventy-four-year-old bankrupt who had experienced a dreadfully long run of bad luck in both his personal life and financial career. The ageing aristocrat believed his continual misfortune to be the product of a long-standing curse that had afflicted his family for seventy-four years. A 'witch of full powers' duly responded to the Duke's printed plea for help and eventually managed to lift the curse. The Duke soon found himself solvent again, and was able to re-enter the realms of high society.

Wanted – Vampire Catcher

Even stranger messages have appeared in the personal columns of newspapers, both national and local, and one such message no doubt caught the attention of thousands of readers in the late summer of 1971. The peculiar eye-catching invitation appeared in a Birmingham newspaper in the first instance, before being printed in the *Daily Mirror* a week afterwards. It began with two questions: 'Do you have an open mind towards the supernatural? Do you have the courage to investigate ghosts and the uncanny? Good pay for the right people. Interested parties should send an SAE to Mr W. Naismith, Lansdowne House, Berkeley Square, London W1X 6AA.'

One of the first people to respond to this intriguing advertisement was twenty-one-year-old Birmingham man, Barry Cody. Unemployed and bored, he'd been trawling through the Situations Vacant pages of his local newspaper. He had vaguely been considering a career as cadet in the Royal Navy, for which he would receive the then princely sum of twenty-one pounds per week, when his attention had been grabbed by the mysterious Mr Naismith's invitation to chase ghosts and ghouls. Barry had been interested in the occult since the age of fifteen, and so he sent a self-addressed envelope to Naismith's address in London, and received an A4-sized piece of paper outlining the type of work involved in Mr William Naismith's Supernatural Investigations Bureau. The pay was attractive at thirty pounds per week, but there were a few conditions. The successful applicant would have to relocate to Berkeley Square in the very desirable district of London's Mayfair, which Barry thought very exciting, but the hours of the job were irregular by their very nature, as ghosts and other supernatural entities do not tend to limit their paranormal activities to a nine to five shift. All the same, Barry was intrigued, it had to be better than sitting around all day doing nothing, and he was definitely sick of being skint. He went for an interview at Berkeley Square and was questioned by seventy-two-year-old Mr Naismith – who was wheelchair-bound – for almost an hour.

Barry was pleased with his performance in the interview and sat waiting for the postman every day until, five days afterwards, the acceptance letter eventually arrived. He was to start work on Wednesday 29 September at 9am and he could barely contain his excitement. Barry and two other successful applicants to the offbeat advertisement – thirty-two-year-old Liz Brookes from Nottingham, and forty-five-year-old Charles Wickham from Bury St Edmunds, met in the ante-room of William Naismith's impressive London residence. An elderly female secretary ushered the trio into a cosy study with carved oak-panelled walls, a grand marble fireplace in which a large fire was blazing, and a long stained-glass window featuring a Latin motto – 'Scientia Deleo Vereor' (knowledge erases fear). As they made themselves comfortable on the beautifully upholstered chairs, their eyes took in their sumptuous new surroundings and they exchanged nervous smiles as they tried to imagine what adventures this strange new world would bring.

The three trainee investigators were served coffee by the secretary, and in this informal atmosphere Mr Naismith talked to them about the principal areas of his research: ghosts, sensory-deprivation, psychometry, doppelgangers, dimensions and ... vampires. It immediately struck Barry Cody that each of the areas of research which Naismith had outlined seemed to have some element of credibility, except for the last – the topic of vampires – which seemed out of place in a scientific establishment and rather outdated to his mind. Somewhat timidly, he expressed his misgivings to his new employer, worried that he might incur his anger, and perhaps even be dismissed on the spot. Instead, Naismith calmly put on a pair of bifocals, retrieved a slim folder from a pile of papers on his desk, and read out a letter from a thirty-eight-year-old Hounslow woman named Mrs Miller, who believed she was being haunted by what she termed a 'biting poltergeist'. For three months, between 10 January and 12 March 1971, Mrs Miller had been awakened in the night by the alarming sensation of being bitten on the neck, breasts and thighs. On two occasions, the unseen biter actually broke the skin of the woman's neck and drew blood. In the end, Mrs Miller had fled her flat in the middle of the night, after seeing the vaporous outline of a man standing over her bed.

William Naismith had investigated Mrs Miller's flat, as well as the flat below hers, which had lain vacant for some time, apparently because it also had a reputation for being haunted by a sinister man in black. This ghost had been active in the flat since the 1920s, according to several elderly people living next door. Mr Naismith was a man of considerable wealth and spared no cost in his thirst for supernatural knowledge. Consequently, he rented both flats for a period of three months, hoping to confront the vampiric entity that had terrified Mrs Miller, and find out its true nature.

He did not have long to wait long, for just one week into his vigil, Naismith encountered the materialisation of a man in late Victorian attire, by candlelight, as he sat in the downstairs flat at 11.50pm. Suspecting the ghost was in fact a vampire, Naismith protected himself by wearing a rosary with a silver crucifix and carrying a phial of holy water, a leather-bound copy of the Holy Bible, several cloves of garlic and a long stake of hawthorn wood. In addition to these items, Naismith had at his disposal a special torch fitted with filaments that gave off ultraviolet light to simulate sunlight – something which was thought to vaporise the skin of a vampire.

However, Naismith never had the chance to test out this novel flashlight, when the suspected vampire rapidly materialised, then attacked him with lightning agility. It had already begun to throttle the elderly investigator, when it suddenly caught sight of the rosary beads and the crucifix around his neck. The effect was immediate. The entity threw Naismith down on to a sofa, as if he were on fire, and ran towards the empty dark mouth of the fireplace and vanished, leaving a musky smell in its wake.

Naismith, an angina sufferer, lay doubled up in pain on the sofa, clutching his chest. He reached into his jacket pocket and brought out a small pill box. He took his angina pill and gradually recovered from the incredible attack, but the experience had taken its toll and he was unable to continue the vigil. Afterwards his health deteriorated and he ended up confined to a wheelchair.

He returned to Berkeley Square and spent days trying to trace a good medium to help him. He found one through the recommendation of a friend – Mrs Ivy Jones of Camden Town. Ivy was taken to the haunted flats in Hounslow during the daytime, to see if she could sense anything amiss. She had only been there for a few minutes when she received distinct impressions of a paradoxical and contradictory nature. She had a vision in which she saw an angelic-faced reverend from long ago delivering a sermon from his pulpit. She believed that he had a surname which sounded like 'Layton'. Despite the man's religious calling and butter-wouldn't-melt-in-his-mouth appearance, this man of the cloth had indulged in bestiality and orgies, as well as having cannibalistic urges. He had interfered with several bodies lying in some sort of chapel of rest, and on one occasion he had even resorted to exhuming the body of a woman, so that he could cut out her heart and eat it roasted.

The medium became so distressed as she tuned into the sinful life of this despicable Victorian clergyman, that she almost fainted, and had to be helped outside by Naismith to be revived in the fresh air. Mrs Jones warned Naismith to, "… leave the flats well alone, because he's evil, and has chosen to walk the darkness, because if he goes across, he'll go straight to Hell."

The medium refused to offer any further help, admitting that she was out of her depth when confronted with such pure evil, but Naismith was determined to lay the vampire to rest once and for all.

Despite listening to this horror story with bated breath, Barry Cody still outwardly rejected the idea that vampires existed, as he did not wish to be seen to back down in front of his new colleagues. Naismith looked him straight in the eye and laid down a challenge: "If you don't believe in vampires, I dare you to stay in the haunted flats for a week. What do you say to that, young man?"

Barry secretly feared that he would meet something inhuman and terrifying in that flat but he did not want to look like a coward, so he accepted the challenge. Naismith gave him a crash course in vampire-slaughtering, and warned him that he should never, under any circumstances, fall for the deceptions of a vampire. In a stern voice the old man said: "They often pretend they are living, breathing human beings, and will beg you to spare their lives. Some use hypnosis to gain the upper hand, so avoid any eye contact. Kill, and ask questions later."

On the last day of September, Barry Cody arrived at the Victorian house, which had been divided into two flats. From the moment the taxi left him at the front door, he had the feeling that he was being watched. He settled down in the ground-floor flat as best he could, all the while mentally reminding himself that there were no such things as vampires, so they couldn't harm him. Instead of burning only candles, as Mr Naismith had instructed, Barry switched on all the lights in the kitchen, bedroom, hall and lounge. Every hour or so he would gingerly tiptoe up the stairs to the upper flat, with the ultraviolet torch in one hand and a Bible in the other and make a cursory inspection of the rooms. He didn't linger and would be back downstairs in the lower flat in less than a minute.

The first part of the night passed without incident, and at around 2.40am, Barry eventually fell into an uneasy sleep as he listened to his transistor radio. On the following evening, at 8.30pm, he heard a noise in the kitchen, and when he went to investigate, he found a boy of about nine or ten years of age prising open the window over the sink and trying to get in. The boy climbed into the kitchen and was startled to see Barry standing in the doorway leading to the hall.

113

"What's your game, lad?" Barry asked the junior intruder, trying to sound confident and masterful.

The boy continued to gaze at him in astonishment for a moment, before stammering out a reply. "I ... I'm looking for my brother ... er Jim," he said nervously.

"Well he isn't here, so beat it," Barry told him, waving him away with the unlit ultraviolet torch.

But the boy didn't move.

"Why are you here?" he asked, standing in the stone sink and looking Barry up and down. He seemed less nervous now.

"Never you mind. Now get out of here before I go and call the police," said Barry. As he spoke these words, he suddenly remembered Naismith's warning and a bizarre thought entered his head – could this child be something inhuman in disguise?

The young trespasser completely ignored Barry and seemed fixated on the adapted torch which he held in his hand, and something about his eyes betrayed a wisdom, a knowingness, that seemed far in advance of his tender years.

Barry switched on the ultraviolet torch and aimed its beam directly at the boy, who let out a shriek as his face instantly turned an ugly dark purplish red and began to blister. He held out his small pale hands to shield his eyes from the scorching beam of synthetic sunlight, and they too turned dark and small black blisters began to erupt all over them. The 'boy' then swung round away from Barry, dived straight through the open window into the darkness of the yard and ran off squealing like a stuck pig.

Barry stood there in shock for a moment, before deciding that enough was enough. What on earth was he doing in this madhouse, putting himself at risk for someone he barely knew? He must be mad. He abandoned his vigil there and then, leaving some of the equipment behind, and headed back to the Supernatural Investigations Bureau in Berkeley Square. Mr Naismith was initially furious at Barry for his "dereliction of duty", as he put it, but later felt more sympathetic towards him. After all, he had been man enough to undertake the dangerous mission in the first place and he couldn't blame him for the way in which he had reacted to something truly terrifying that was outside of most people's everyday experience. After all, it had been more than a match for himself. In fact it had nearly finished him off.

The second vigil at the haunted flats took place three days later, and on this occasion, Liz Brookes joined Barry Cody, who had somehow been persuaded that there was safety in numbers and that if they followed Naismith's instructions to the letter, they would be safe. At 10.45pm on the very first night of the 'vampire watch' Barry and Liz heard slow footsteps coming from the upstairs flat and looked at each other for reassurance. Remembering that it was their job to tackle just such situations as this, they went upstairs to investigate, both in an understandably anxious state. They checked out the lounge first, and found nothing amiss there, then proceeded to the bedroom, where an overpoweringly sweet smell, possibly of lavender, filled the air. An old pine wardrobe stood in the corner, and Liz's attention was immediately drawn to it. She stared at it for a couple of seconds, then abruptly turned towards the bedroom door, pulling Barry by his elbow after her.

"What's wrong?" Barry whispered, instinctively knowing that something had spooked his colleague. "Did you see something horrible in that wardrobe?"

Liz completely ignored his questions and hurtled down the stairs, two at a time. Not until she had entered the downstairs flat and locked the door behind them, did she reveal what had chilled her.

"Oh my God!" she whispered. "That was him! He's up there in that old wardrobe."

"What do you mean? What did you see?"

"Ssh! Keep your voice down, or he'll hear us," she hissed, terror etched on her face.

She told Barry that when she had glanced at the wardrobe, she had noticed that its door had been slightly ajar, and two grey-looking fingers had been slightly protruding from the gap in the door.

"Someone was inside that wardrobe, I swear to God. He was keeping the door closed over with his first and second fingers."

"I've had enough of this," said Barry. "I'd rather be a shelf stacker in Tescos than put up with this lot every day. It's a total joke. Naismith can find his own vampires. I'm getting out."

Liz was just about to agree, when she and Barry heard footsteps in the upstairs flat once again. They stood stock still, scarcely daring to breathe. The footsteps were coming down the stairs – to the ground floor flat! A rattling sound was heard in the hallway. The thing from upstairs was doing something to the fuse-box in the communal hallway. It must have removed the fuses, because seconds later, the flats were plunged into total darkness.

In a confused daze, Barry rummaged through his holdall and by his sense of touch alone, located the eighteen-inch hawthorn stake and the wooden mallet and grabbed them both. Liz's trembling hands seized the ultraviolet torch. She fumbled with the switch but the torch wouldn't seem to work. The filaments must have burnt out, or broken. With rising panic she felt around and located a full size Gordon's Gin bottle filled with holy water, and a wooden cross.

The door burst open and in a heartbeat something knocked Liz to the ground. She tried to scream but the scream was stifled by a pair of cold lips and a thin wet tongue pressing into her open mouth. Strong icy cold hands grabbed her throat and chest, pinning her to the ground. Barry was overcome by intense nausea as he stumbled towards the shadowy thing covering his colleague. Lifting the wooden hawthorn stake as high as he could, he brought it crashing down into the hollow of its back and then slammed the mallet down on top of it. But the wooden hammer glanced off the head of the stake and struck his thumb instead. Barry's abortive attempt at staking the vampiric being at least had the effect of distracting it for a moment, and in that fleeting window of opportunity, Liz lashed out with the holy water-filled gin bottle and smashed it on the supernatural attacker's head.

That seemed to succeed where Barry's attempt had failed and her weird assailant let out a long agonised shriek. They then heard him running out of the room and down the hallway towards the kitchen.

Barry helped Liz to her feet and the two of them hurried out into the street via the front door. This all took place in the days when mobile phones were unheard of, and so the two amateur vampire hunters had to find a public telephone box to call William Naismith. Even after he had heard their terrifying account he had the cheek to ask them to return to the flats immediately to put the fuses back into the fusebox. Liz and Barry flatly refused to enter that house until the following morning, when the light of dawn had evaporated their fears of the night before and would offer some protection against any further attacks.

However, after that eventful night, there were no further peculiar goings-on at the Hounslow flats. It was as if the vampire (and the possible vampiric child) had had enough; they had met their match in the gallant young pair and had left to seek another lair.

Research has shown that a Reverend Layton certainly did live at the house in Hounslow in the 1890s, so perhaps the medium Ivy Jones was right. By what process then, did the warped and depraved reverend turn into a vampire after his death? Occult lore states that those who have died by committing suicide, certain witches, evil murderers, men of the cloth who have been excommunicated because they have turned to the Devil, and those bitten by a vampire, are all at risk of becoming vampires themselves forty days after their death. It is not hard to imagine the post-death fate of the soul of such a man as the evil reverend who, during his lifetime, molested dead bodies entrusted into his spiritual care, who ate a dead woman's heart, and engaged in sexual intercourse with animals. Even by vampire standards, the reverend was evidently a thoroughly rotten specimen.

VAMPIRES OF THE ROAD

THE LONE NIGHT DRIVER knows only two well how the roads and highways can be deceptive and appear so different during the hours of darkness. The motorist's mind after nightfall becomes more susceptible to fatigue – and therefore to all kinds of tricks of the imagination – our worst enemy at night. Some drivers combat this fear by turning on the car radio, or CD player and so blot out those niggling fears which tend to creep in on a dark and lonely road. The passing landscapes glimpsed at either side of the road, and the roads themselves bathed in the light of the sodium lamps, take on a different appearance after dark and can become quite eerie. The shadow of a gnarled oak tree may be perceived as the outline of some monstrous or supernatural entity, but sometimes such perceptions are by no means all in the mind. Without a doubt, paranormal entities exist, which haunt the highways and byways of Britain, and a small number of these may actually be vampires.

The Life and Death of Black Tom

Union Street, in Bedford, runs close to the town's category B prison, and at the point where this street meets Tavistock Street and Clapham Road, you will these days find an innocuous-looking roundabout. Yet beneath this roundabout lies a staked corpse: the mortal remains of a vampiric highwayman nicknamed Black Tom, who was hanged for highway robbery in 1607.

Strange rumours surrounded this bandit, who earned his nickname because of his swarthy, almost yellowish-green skin and coal-black hair. Some claimed he was a vampire, while others believed that he had sold his soul to the Devil. The authorities were warned by the superstitious people of Bedford that Black Tom would rise from his grave if he wasn't staked, and so, after his body was removed from the gallows, a man approached with a large hammer and a sharpened wooden stake, four inches in diameter and almost two feet in length. In front of a huge mob, who treated such grisly proceedings as entertainment, he tore open the dead man's shirt, exposing his bare chest, then pushed the point of the stake into the corpse's breastbone. A volunteer held the stake in place, whilst the man brought down the hammer hard seven times. This caused blood to issue from the mouth, nose and anus of the corpse, and wind that was expelled from its stomach and intestines gave several of the onlookers more than they bargained for, showering them with blood and mucous. The corpse then started to shudder with post-death nerves, and it was then turned over on to its stomach so that Black Tom would be facing Hell when he was lowered into his deep grave.

People spat vehemently down the hole as the gravediggers were trying to fill it, and that should have been the end of the demonic highwayman, but it was only the beginning. Black Tom would outlive everyone who had stood at his graveside that day, including the man who had driven the stake through his heart. For somehow the highwayman who had been rumoured to thirst for blood during his lifetime, managed to escape from his grave, and was seen by many of the terrified people of the town, dressed in a long black cape with his head lolling about as he walked – probably because the hangman's noose had broken his neck.

One evening, in 1608, the vampire is said to have jumped on to the back of a horse being ridden by a well-to-do lady across a common, just as the last rays of the sun were disappearing below the horizon. The lady's name was Susanna Higgins, and she was subjected to a violent attack by none other than Black Tom, come back from the dead to terrorise the living. Violently wrestling her to the ground, the fiend bit deeply into her breasts, neck and thighs. Miss Higgins was only saved by the arrival on the scene of John Gibbons, a gentleman who happened to be passing in a stagecoach at the time of the assault and who heard her cries and called the stagecoach to a halt. Gibbons gave chase but the caped assailant vanished into the dusk.

The vampire attacks of Black Tom continued for over two centuries, and at one point, seven priests and a gang of local men and women even attempted to ambush the blood-thirsty highwayman, so that they could impale him and burn him at the stake, but he managed to give them the slip and ran off under the cover of darkness at a superhuman speed. Black Tom was encountered by the unwary right up until the 1960s, according to the folklore of Bedfordshire.

In 1963, George Johnson, a motorist from St Albans, ran into the vampire and knocked him down. This happened during the severe winter of 1963, when Mr Johnson was driving along Bedford's Tavistock Street towards his brother-in-law's house on Clapham Road. The time was just after 10pm and a sudden heavy snowfall made driving very difficult. Fortunately, the road ahead was deserted, because the windscreen of Mr Johnson's Ford Anglia had become coated with large snowflakes and his visibility was suddenly and drastically reduced. Even with the windscreen wipers switched on to maximum, he was finding it very difficult to see, because the snow was coming down so quickly.

Suddenly, out of nowhere, the fuzzy outline of a pedestrian came into view and dashed straight into the path of the vehicle. Johnson pushed the brakes to the floor and immediately went into a skid, hitting the person square on with a sickening thud. He rolled across the bonnet of the car, up and over the windscreen and then over the top of the roof. Johnson watched, horrified, as the person slid down the rear window and landed in the road like a rag doll.

The car having skidded to a halt, George Johnson got out and proceeded to walk towards the back of the Ford Anglia, his heart in his mouth. What had he done? Was the man dead?

Lying in a crumpled heap on the thin layer of fresh snow was the strangest figure imaginable; he was dressed in black and his old-fashioned theatre cloak fanned out across the road. George's first thought was that he had knocked down an actor on his way home from the theatre, still wearing his theatrical costume. Then he noticed the man's deeply lined face and it made him shudder. There was something revolting about it that he couldn't quite put his finger on – something evil, menacing, not quite human. His hands too looked shrivelled, dried up, ancient, almost like the Egyptian mummies he used to enjoy looking at when he was taken to the museum as a child.

As George Johnson stooped down beside the man to check whether he was still alive by feeling for a pulse, he suddenly opened his eyes, giving George the fright of his life. The eyes were startlingly bloodshot with pitch-black irises. The ghastly-looking eyes then swivelled in their sockets to survey Johnson, boring into him from head to toe. Johnson shrank back under the penetrating stare, sensing that there was something very very wrong about this man. Even so, he couldn't dispute the fact that he had knocked him down and so he was about to call for an ambulance, when the odd-looking man suddenly made the most miraculous recovery. Without a word, he jumped to his feet ran off into the snowstorm, with the sprightly step of a much younger man.

George Johnson stood there for quite some time not knowing what to do next, or what to make of the whole weird incident. Should he report the accident to the police? Then again, where was the accident victim now? and what would they make of his story anyway? They would probably think he was mad, or drunk. He was so confused about the whole affair himself, that he eventually decided to leave it be and continue on his journey home.

When he reached the home of his brother-in-law, Bob, he mentioned the bizarre heart-stopping collision with the eccentric red-eyed pedestrian, and to his surprise, Bob told him that the same man had been seen in the area many times before over the years, and was supposed to be the vampire highwayman Black Tom. George Johnson remembered the intense unnatural redness of the old man's eyes and the apparent advanced age of his heavily wrinkled face, and shuddered. He didn't doubt for a minute that the figure he had knocked down was indeed Black Tom and that he had had a very lucky escape.

In the late 1960s, two amateur ghost-hunters investigated the alleged sightings of the resurrected seventeenth century highwayman and came to the conclusion that the vampire had a secret lair in a wooded area close to the A6 motorway. A vampire hunt was planned but the authorities got wind of what they saw as nothing more than a 'publicity stunt' and cautioned the ghost investigators against proceeding any further with their plan.

Perhaps Black Tom is now resting in peace at last, as he hasn't been seen or heard of since 1969 – or is he simply hibernating, waiting for an opportunity to restart his nefarious activities?

The following strange story was related to me in September 2001, by a Liverpool comedian whom I cannot identify. He stipulated that he would only relate the full facts of this bizarre and scary tale if I would give him my word that I would never identify him. I shall therefore have to call the comedian 'Bob'.

Nightclub Nightmare

In the early 1990s, Bob, a popular Liverpool comedian, drove up the M62 one evening to Manchester, where he was due to perform a comedy routine in a club, as part of a cabaret show. As usual, Bob's performance was very warmly received by his audience, and so he decided to go back on stage for a further twenty minutes. Whilst Bob was performing his additional material, to the great delight of his fans, he noticed a beautiful-looking woman of about twenty-five to thirty years of age sitting at one of the tables. She was laughing at all Bob's jokes, just like everybody else, but she was also smiling at him in a very sexual and flirtatious way. She was very attractive and reminded the comedian of the film actress Farrah Fawcett Majors, who had enjoyed some popularity in the 1970s.

After the comedy act, Bob went backstage and changed his clothes, then the manager of the club escorted him to a specially-reserved table where he was to be served with a meal and a drink. Just before the next performer took to the stage, Bob went over to the table were the woman was sitting alone, and asked her if she would like to join him. The woman smiled warmly and accepted his invitation without hesitation. She was very tall and slim and very elegant and looked even more attractive at closer quarters. She had striking sapphire-blue eyes and long blonde hair. In a soft, sexy voice, she introduced herself, "My name's Danielle." Bob couldn't quite place her accent but it was definitely not a local one.

He ordered a bottle of champagne and was soon chatting up Danielle, who seemed to be very receptive to his attentions, although she was singularly unimpressed by his champagne gesture and said that she preferred to sip mineral water. There was a 'stay-behind' at the club that night, and it wasn't long before Bob and Danielle were embracing on the dance floor as they danced to all the slow numbers. Bob had learned from Danielle that her boyfriend had arranged to meet her at the club, but hadn't turned up for some reason. She told him that she lived in St Helens, on the outskirts of Liverpool, to which Bob replied that, as she had not been drinking, she might like to drive him home to Liverpool in his car. Danielle suggested that it would be better for Bob to stay overnight at her home, until he was fit enough to drink in the morning, but in the end, they agreed to go to Bob's.

At 3am, Bob and Danielle left the club in Manchester and walked through the chilly night air towards the club car park. Danielle was shivering in her skimpy sleeveless top, so in a gentlemanly gesture, Bob took off his leather jacket and put it round her shoulders. Minutes later, the couple embarked on the return journey down the M62. Danielle had to fasten Bob's seatbelt for him because he was too intoxicated to do it for himself. During the journey, the mood unaccountably changed and Danielle stared at the road ahead in stony silence, making Bob feel very uncomfortable. So he reached for the controls of the car radio, hoping to find some music to lighten the atmosphere inside the vehicle, but Danielle's hand intercepted his and prevented him from switching on the radio. He was too drunk to make an effective protest and so the couple sat in silence as the car sped along the motorway.

Something suddenly made Bob feel even more uneasy and he took a peek at Danielle from the corner of his eye. He saw something that still gives him nightmares to this day. The girl's beautiful features had undergone the most startling transformation, into what can only be described as a demonic face. She turned to face him, and by the light of the powerful motorway floodlights, he could see that the whites of her eyes had turned blood red, and her mouth had opened wide – twice as wide as any normal human mouth and more like a snake's – to reveal an array of long pointed teeth.

The comedian sobered up in an instant. He felt faint and breathless with the shock of finding himself in a car being driven by some sort of supernatural entity resembling a vampiress. The silence was broken when the thing sitting in his driving seat suddenly became horribly animated, screaming with laughter and suicidally zig-zagging between the lanes of the motorway and the other vehicles. Bob was not a religious man, but he suddenly found himself repeating the phrase, "Jesus, please save me" over and over again under his breath.

The car suddenly screeched into a 180-degree turn and slid off the hard shoulder and on to a slip road, where it veered off into a ditch, landing at a crazy angle. Bob opened the door and frantically tried to get out, but in his blind panic, he forgot to unclick his seatbelt, so he sat there struggling like a rat in a trap. He shouted out for help, but there was no one there to hear his cries, just empty fields, jet black except for the few feet next to the road.

Still struggling, he looked at the seat beside him; it was empty, except for his leather jacket. There was no trace of the fanged fiend that had been masquerading as a woman and who had subjected him to a white knuckle ride in his own car.

The police found Bob wandering along the hard shoulder of the M62 in a very distressed state later that night. He related his bizarre tale to the officers, realising that it sounded ridiculously far-fetched and, just as he had expected, he wasn't believed. The police did, however, check out his story with the nightclub, and the management confirmed that he had left with a woman answering the description he had given them and that she had agreed to drive him home. Not one person at the club had any idea who 'Danielle' was and she was never seen there again. Bob was very badly shaken by the spine-chilling incident, and has never appeared at the Manchester club since.

Every so often, Bob relives the horror of that night with the vampiric woman in his dreams, and on more than one occasion he has woken up in a cold sweat, struggling to get out of the car. He has no idea why the entity chose to pick on him that night, and he wonders what fate he would have met had he not called upon Jesus to save him.

The case is a real puzzler. Is Danielle still out there waiting to perform her devilish transfiguration trick on some other unsuspecting male one day? Only time will tell.

Strange Slayings

I Want to Live Forever

IN NOVEMBER 2001, Mabel Leyshon, a harmless old lady of ninety years of age, was viciously stabbed to death at her home in Llanfairpwll on Anglesey. Her killer was found to be seventeen-year-old Mathew Hardman – Mrs Leyshon's former newspaper delivery boy. This callous youth had not only stabbed the deaf pensioner twenty-two times, but had also mutilated her body in the grossest way and had finished his handiwork by placing two pokers at her feet in the shape of a cross.

An even more appalling discovery was made by the policemen sent to investigate the murder – the dead woman's excised heart was found next to her body, wrapped in newspaper, like some discarded portion of fish and chips, and then stuffed into a saucepan. Of this macabre ritualistic crime, sickened police officer Detective Superintendent Alan Jones told reporters that the injuries were the worst he had ever seen in his career. The police subsequently discovered that the teenaged killer had also drunk some of the blood of his elderly victim, apparently in an effort to acquire immortality.

During the trial, and before Mr Justice Richards had pronounced that Hardman should be detained at Her Majesty's pleasure (a life sentence), the prosecution had explained to the jury how he had been obsessed with vampires and the darker side of the Occult. Just two months before the horrific murder, Hardman had accused a sixteen-year-old German exchange student of being a vampire. He had then tried to persuade the girl to bite into his neck, so that he too could become a vampire. When she refused, Hardman allegedly forced his neck against her mouth and the student had to shout for help. Hardman denied that he was obsessed with vampires and claimed that his curiosity regarding the nocturnal bloodsuckers was merely a "subtle interest".

Justice Richards told Hardman that the attack on Mrs Leyshon had clearly been planned and carefully calculated, then told him, "Why you, an otherwise pleasant and well regarded young man, should act in this way is difficult to comprehend. You had hoped for immortality. All you achieved was to brutally end another person's life and the bringing of a life sentence upon yourself."

The jury took four hours to reach a verdict in a trial which was so graphically gruesome, that journalists had great difficulty reporting the gory details of the case in a manner which did not offend public decency. When the verdict was announced, Hardman wept in the dock at Mold Crown Court and his mother's screams filled the courthouse.

What could possibly have driven a seemingly normal teenager to smash his way into an innocent pensioner's home and then to stab her twenty-two times, before slicing open her chest to pull out her heart? Hardman had, in the words of the prosecution, an obsessive preoccupation with vampires, but surely this was not sufficient incentive to commit such a terrible crime.

What is even more disturbing is that this was not a unique case. In his book, *The Anatomy of Crime*, the celebrated Superintendent Robert Fabian of Scotland Yard, one of the most hard-boiled logical and scientific detectives in the history of criminology, wrote a curious paragraph about one particular murder case that he never solved:

I advise anybody who is tempted at any time to venture into Black Magic, witchcraft, Shamanism – call it what you will – to remember Charles Walton and to think of his death, which was clearly the ghastly climax of a pagan rite. There is no stronger argument for keeping as far away as possible from the villains with their swords, incense and mumbo-jumbo. It is prudence on which your future peace of mind and even your life could depend.

In his warning to the idly curious, Fabian was referring to the baffling case of the 'Pitchfork Murder', which occurred in 1945 in the village of Lower Quinton, just a few miles south of Stratford-upon-Avon. Before we look into the murder mystery, we must first go back in time to 1662 to understand why the area around the scene of the crime is so steeped in witchcraft.

Witch Hunt

In the spring of 1662, Isobel Gowdie, a Scottish witch, was burned at the stake for using a team of harnessed toads to pull a miniature plough across a field. In Celtic mythology, the toad has always been associated with witchcraft, sorcery and curses and blights, and this symbolism was carried on into Christianity. In Greek lore, Amerindian legend, and even Chinese mythology, the toad was also regarded as a magical creature, identified with the powers of darkness, so nobody in seventeenth century Scotland thought it at all reprehensible to put an old woman to death for employing toads to pull a toy plough.

Throughout the rest of Britain, the toad was a much-maligned yet respected creature. In the English Fens, for example, a peculiar Roman tradition still survives – the practice of using a toad as a compass. This custom dates back to the days when the occupying Romans would lay a dagger on a toad's back, then watch the creature move around slowly until it stopped when the dagger pointed due north.

Over two centuries after the execution of Isobel Gowdie, another old woman who was suspected of being a witch was also put to death. She was seventy-five-year-old Ann Tenant of Long Compton in Warwickshire. John Heywood, the youth who slayed her, had severe learning difficulties and was referred to locally as the 'village idiot'. Heywood had become convinced that Miss Tenant was a member of a coven of witches who held their sabbats in the countryside around the village of Long Compton. Some said the old woman also employed toads to blight people's crops by black magic rituals.

At the murder trial, Heywood quickly confessed to the murder, "Her was a proper witch. I pinned her to the ground [with a pitchfork] before slashing her throat with a bill-hook to carve a cross."

Local gossip at the time of the trial had it that Long Compton was becoming the epicentre of witchcraft in the region, and an old saying of the day was: "There are enough witches in Long Compton to draw a wagonload of hay up Long Compton Hill".

Strangely enough, just south of this village stands a circle of

Neolithic or Bronze Age stones, known as the Rollright Stones, which have been associated with pagan rituals for centuries. Even today, modern witches and occultists still gather within the circle of stones to conduct their esoteric rites.

The Pitchfork Murder

About fifteen miles north of the Rollright Stones, the picturesque village of Lower Quinton sits in the shadow of Meon Hill. Even today, Lower Quinton has a spooky aura about it after dark, and is surrounded by eerily-named places such as Devil's Elbow and Upper Slaughter.

In a thatched cottage at Lower Quinton in the 1940s, lived seventy-four-year-old Charles Walton and his unmarried niece Edith. In his younger days, Walton had worked as a ploughman, but now in old age his joints were plagued with stabbing rheumatism, and he was forced to eke out a meagre living by putting in a seven-hour day for one shilling and sixpence an hour, hedge-cutting for local farmers. He was a familiar figure in the village, easily recognisable from a distance by his double-pronged hay-fork which he held over his shoulder and his slash-hook which he carried in his hand, as he hobbled to work up Meon Hill. Outwardly there was nothing to suggest that the old hedger and ditcher was anything out of the ordinary, but Walton had a dark side. He had acquired quite a sinister reputation in the village, where it was common knowledge that he bred huge warty toads and was once a horse whisperer of some repute.

Horse whispering is the ancient, and now largely forgotten art of being able to control a horse from a distance without any word of command. Those who have the skill need only a slight gesture of the hand to make the horse stay, run, canter or gallop. Walton's horse whispering abilities were so amazing, that they seemed nothing short of witchcraft to the superstitious locals, and his power over animals allegedly extended to cattle, toads and birds. What's more, it was said that Walton had been spotted on many occasions imitating the songs of the nightingale and chirping to other species of bird. He openly professed to be conversant in the aeolian language of his feathered friends, for they seemed to obey his requests to refrain from eating the seeds sown in the fields of his little plot, which flourished in a way that his neighbours' did not.

On the morning of 14 February 1945, Charles Walton left home as usual with his hedging tools and hobbled off up Meon Hill to attend to the hedges that formed the border of Alfred Potter's farm, about a mile from Walton's cottage.

By six o'clock that evening, Edith began to worry about her uncle, as he still hadn't returned from work, and he was usually back home before four o'clock. She felt that something terrible must have happened to him, and suspected that he had collapsed, as he had recently been complaining about the unbearable rheumatic pain that was crippling his legs. Edith sought out her neighbour, Harry Beasley and told him of her concerns. He was sure that she was worrying over nothing, but he could see that she was upset and so he agreed to go with her. They both hiked up Meon's Hill to Potter's farm – known as 'The Firs' – Edith with a mounting sense of trepidation; something inside her was telling her that something was badly amiss.

Farmer Potter told Edith and Harry that he had seen someone in the distance earlier in the day who appeared to be cutting hedges, and he had assumed that it was Walton. However, he thought that Walton must have long gone home by now. He fetched a flashlight from the barn and led Walton's niece and her neighbour over the fields to the spot where the old man had last been seen. None of them was prepared for what they were about to see.

The spotlight of the torch picked out every detail of the whole horrific scene. Lying under a willow tree, near the top of Meon Hill, was the spread-eagled body of Charles Walton. Potter took one glance at the corpse then quickly shielded Edith from the full horror of the gruesome sight with his arm and then escorted her home and found someone to sit with her. He then summoned the police.

Meanwhile, back at the scene of the crime, Harry Beasley nervously stood guard over his murdered neighbour. Walton had died a particularly brutal death, having been impaled with his own pitch fork. The twin prongs of the tool had been driven through his neck with such force, that they had penetrated the ground beneath to a depth of six inches. Crosses had been carved on Walton's cheeks, neck and abdomen, and the bill-hook that had been used to cut out the symbols was still wedged between his ribs. Near to the body lay the old man's walking stick, now covered in blood, because it had been used to bludgeon his head to a pulp. The face of Charles Walton was frozen in an expression of sheer terror.

The Warwickshire police force reacted very oddly to the unusual crime. They seemed to be strangely reluctant to investigate, and instead called for a murder squad from Scotland Yard to look into the killing. On the following day, Detective Superintendent Robert Fabian and his assistant, Detective Sergeant Albert Webb, turned up at the village and were immediately greeted with what appeared to be a conspiracy of silence. The few locals who were prepared to divulge anything at all, merely told Fabian that Walton had been a secretive, strange old man, who bred large natterjack toads in the damp undergrowth of his garden. Fabian also managed to glean that Walton had never been over-fond of company, and had bought his cider by the gallon from local pubs and preferred to drink it either alone, or with Edith, by his kitchen fireside.

Fabian could not allow his judgement to be clouded by superstition, yet he was convinced that Walton had been ritually murdered, so he took the unprecedented step of consulting Dr Margaret Murray, a witchcraft and vampire expert, and he also delved into the local history of the area. He was particularly intrigued to uncover a record from 1875 of the murder of Ann Tenant, who had been killed in practically the same manner as Charles Walton. Fabian began to suspect that the person, or persons, who had killed Walton had carried out the murder in order to purge the village of a man who had been regarded as a practising witch; hence the wall of silence.

However, he kept all his options open and the line of inquiry switched to the prisoner-of-war camp over at Long Marston for a time, where Italian, German and Slavonic soldiers were quizzed in relation to the crime. At the end of this process, Fabian was confident that they were all innocent of Walton's murder.

Then something even weirder happened. A black dog was found hanged on Meon Hill. There were hushed claims in the village that the hound had been Walton's 'familiar' – a demon in disguise. Even the secular-minded Fabian was unnerved by the hanged dog, because on the first day of the murder investigation he had climbed Meon Hill to examine the crime scene, and had been intrigued to notice a large black retriever that was seated on a nearby wall, watching him intently. Seconds afterwards, a boy walked past and Fabian asked, "Are you looking for your dog, son?"

The boy returned the question with a blank stare and then asked, "What dog?"

Fabian suddenly noticed that the dog had vanished, and the boy, who had obviously been raised by superstitious parents, careered off down the hill in absolute terror. He later spread the word amongst the villagers that Fabian had seen the infamous ghostly black dog, which was widely regarded as a portent of death or bad luck.

Shortly after the hanged dog was cut down from the tree, another dog was run over by a police car, followed by a spate of inexplicable canine deaths throughout the murder investigation. As if to underline the relevance of the canine coincidences, Fabian's attention was drawn to a curious passage in an old yellowed book entitled *Folklore, Old Customs and Superstitions in Shakespeare Land*, which was written in 1930. The text of the passage actually referred to the young Charles Walton:

At Alveston a plough named Charles Walton met a dog on his way home nine times in successive evenings. He told both the shepherd and the carter with whom he worked, and was laughed at for his pains. On the ninth encounter a headless lady rushed past him in a silk dress, and on the next day he heard of his sister's death.

Fabian and Webb learned from several of the more talkative villagers that in early spring 1944, crops had been unusually slow in growing, and there were several fatal accidents involving livestock. The harvest was a disaster and even the beer had unaccountably turned sour in all the local pubs. Many were sure that the source of the widespread run of bad luck was down to Walton, so Fabian naturally deduced that the old man had been slain in order to put an end to his evil magical influences. That person or persons had probably had an intimate knowledge of the occult and would have planned the murder months in advance. Fabian

131

was aware that the date of Walton's death – 14 February – was Valentine's Day, and occasionally Ash Wednesday, but that particular date also held a special relevance to the ancient Druids, as they carried out human sacrifices on that day to procure a good harvest.

Fabian of the Yard finally had to concede defeat. Four thousand statements had been taken and painstakingly cross-referenced; twenty-nine samples of blood, skin and hair were analysed, but all to no avail, and the wall of silence in the village proved to be impenetrable to the London policemen. And so Fabian and Webb were reluctantly forced to retreat to the capital, where more mundane crimes were demanding their attention.

For many years afterwards, Robert Fabian would return to Lower Quinton on the anniversary of the Walton killing and hide himself amongst the undergrowth on Meon Hill to keep a watch on the site of the murder, perhaps hoping that the killer would return to the scene of the crime on the anniversary, but no one ever did. Speaking of the Walton murder to a newspaper in 1976, the then retired Fabian told a reporter: "Detectives deal in facts, but I must admit there was something uncanny about that investigation."

Was Charles Walton really a witch, or even a vampire, as some of those who have studied the case have suggested? It is difficult to give a definitive answer to such questions after such a long period of time has elapsed. There was undoubtedly a ritualistic aspect to the slaying, and the ulterior motive seems to lie somewhere in the occult sphere. Someone reading this book may hold the answer to the riddle, but he or she may prefer to keep that skeleton firmly locked in the cupboard.

Vampire Hunting in Warwickshire

In the county of Warwickshire, where Walton was murdered, there is an old mid-nineteenth century tale about three men who tracked a notorious vampire and tortured it mercilessly in an effort to get the sadistic bloodthirsty fiend to reveal the whereabouts of its lair, in which it was believed that others of its kind were living.

They finally came upon him just as the last vestiges of the sun's light were disappearing at a secluded spot on the banks of the River Avon.

The river bank was edged with willows, and it was here that the vampire – formally a doctor named Paxton – was shot through the head with a crossbow bolt made of hawthorn, a wood traditionally used to combat such creatures of the night.

However, the men had not bargained for the resilience of the vampire and the injured Paxton refused to die. Clutching the gaping wound in his head, he tried to make a run for it in order to escape the trio of vampire hunters – Matthias Green, Jim Sherring, and a librarian from Stratford named Bindley, who was something of an expert on vampirology. Bindley knew that vampires abhorred water, and so, as Paxton backed away towards the banks of the Avon, the librarian realised that the creature was trapped, as nothing would persuade it to jump into the river. Matthias Green, a mercenary in the pay of a local committee of farmers, unleashed several more bolts from his crossbow, two of which hit the vampire squarely in the chest and neck. The creature howled in agony, lost its footing on the slippery bank and then slid into the river, where it disappeared from sight in the low night mists that drifted above the still waters.

Jim Sherring, a local poacher, took off his outer clothes and dived into the river. He dived over and over again until he located Paxton. It was all that he could do to drag the vampire out of the river, for, although he was incapacitated as far as escape was concerned, he was still struggling and thrashing about. Having got him out, Sherring and Matthias Green then hanged him from the branch of a tree. By this time a full moon had risen from behind the trees and by its ghostly light the three men attempted to interrogate the vile fanged freak as to the whereabouts of its lair, but the vampire only hissed and spat at them and attempted to claw at their faces with its long yellowed talons, all the while emitting the most spine-chilling shrieks.

Bindley then directed the mercenary to carry out one of the most horrific acts of torture known to man – the 'Blood Eagle'. This barbaric stomach-churning atrocity was carried out on such historical personages as King Ella of Northumbria in March 867 AD, as well as King Edmund and King Maelgualai of Munster. Matthias Green did not hesitate for a moment. Taking a long razor-sharp knife from his pocket, he proceeded to slash open the back of vampire Paxton from the nape of his neck to his buttocks. This being done, he then calmly pulled aside the long gash to expose the spine of the nocturnal parasite. The vampire screamed for mercy, and a second vampire, hearing the screams, suddenly appeared from behind a tree some three hundred yards away.

With blood-slicked hands Matthias loaded a hawthorn bolt into his crossbow and fired it at Paxton's confederate but he missed his target and the shadowy figure darted away at the last moment. The mercenary then turned back to his other task. This time, taking a broad-bladed knife, he detached the ribs of the hanged, but still conscious, vampire and opened the rib cages right out, so that they resembled the bloodstained eagles 'wings' from which this heinous act derives its name.

The vampire squealed like a stuck pig and his tortured body went into convulsions. The poacher Sherring gloated at the death throes of the vampire, while Bindley grimaced as Matthias Green thrust his hands deep inside the vampire's bleeding chest and ripped out the lungs of the humanoid leech. The vampire made a loud rasping sound before the soldier of fortune decided at last to show a modicum of compassion, by swiftly hammering a wooden steak through its heart, which finally put an end to the creature's ordeal.

The vampire's corpse was painstakingly dismembered and then thrown on a fire which burned continuously until the first rays of dawn threw light on the scene of so much destruction.

Despite all their efforts, the location of the vampire's lair was never discovered and so Paxton's blood-lusting brothers were never captured and so evaded the fate of their companion in blood. This nest of vampires allegedly prowled Warwickshire for many years, causing fear and panic wherever they struck.

Bindley the vampire specialist was said to have himself been killed by a vampiric entity near Aconbury, a small village in Herefordshire. The murder supposedly took place at midnight on Twelfth Night, when the shocking outline of a man which formed out of a plume of blue smoke that had drifted up from a bubbling well. Bindley desperately rummaged about in his knapsack for a crucifix with which to repel the partially materialised form, of what appeared to be a monk in a cowl. Wilson, Bindley's fourteen-year-old assistant, ran off at this point, terrified by what he had seen. When he finally plucked up enough courage to return, he found the librarian lying dead with an appalling bloody wound to his neck. The body was found to contain not a single drop of blood, yet there was no pool of blood surrounding the body, or issuing from the neck.

The vampire is said to haunt Aconbury churchyard to this day, and its wraith-like form has been seen lingering close to the tomb of Roger de Clifford for some unknown reason.

AN IRISH VAMPIRE IN ENGLAND

The Legacy of Crom Cruach

IN COUNTY CAVAN IN IRELAND, in the late nineteenth century, a certain priest, Father Randall, went to see his local doctor to investigate the source of a nagging pain in his side and a constant ticklish cough, both of which he had been ignoring for some time. The doctor gave the priest a full examination and then told him to get dressed. After sitting his patient back down, and with a grave face, he said, "I'm afraid the news is not good, Father. Why didn't you come to see me before? You have got advanced tuberculosis, and I'm afraid the disease has gone past the point of being treatable."

"Oh dear! How long have I got, doctor?"

"Difficult to say, but probably about three months, perhaps four," the doctor replied sombrely. "I'm very sorry, Father."

The doctor's grim estimate proved to be all too correct and the priest died within a few months.

Ironically, Father Randall's mother was said to be a witch, who practised the darkest form of black magic. She had fallen out with her son long ago because he had opposed her beliefs and chosen to follow the path of Christ. Nevertheless, when the priest passed away from consumption, his mother held a wake for him, and on the second night of this age-old ritual, when all the mourners had gone back to their homes, she invoked demons to resurrect her son. The demons agreed to grant her wish but they demanded a very high price in return – Mrs Randall's own life. A mother's love for her son is a very powerful thing, no matter what has gone between them and she agreed to sacrifice her own life in return for his. The demons took it accordingly, exactly a year after Father Randall's resurrection.

The priest awoke in his open coffin in the early hours of the morning following the wake and his first act was to violently fling the rosary beads that had been placed in his fist across the room. He was confused and a little afraid at first, as he slowly came to his senses, and he decided to visit his old friend Father Hanlon, an elderly priest in a neighbouring parish, whom he had always liked and trusted. Perhaps he could explain how and why he had been brought back to life.

Father Hanlon soon realised that there was something very amiss. For a start, Randall couldn't bear to look at a crucifix and he seemed equally on edge when his gaze fell upon the Holy Bible, or indeed, any of the other religious artefacts in his study. Of course, these were all things which the old Father Randall would have previously treated with the utmost reverence. With a sinking heart, the old priest immediately suspected that Randall had been resurrected as a vampire.

Father Hanlon was knowledgeable about vampires from personal experience, and was well aware of the stance which the Catholic Church took regarding them: that is that most of them were mere delusions, but that some were dead bodies reanimated by Satan to carry out his wicked schemes on earth. The Vatican had decreed that suspected vampires of the latter type should be exhumed from their graves and burned until not a vestige of them remained. No compassion was to be shown towards such ex-humans, according to the Vatican hierarchy. It must be understood that these were laws laid down in an era when babies who died before baptism were staked through the heart to prevent them becoming 'minor demons' in Hell. In our more enlightened times this barbaric law has been repealed, and the Church now believes that such infants are totally free from Original Sin, and as such they will return straight to God after death.

Father Hanlon had a long talk with the vampiric ex-priest and advised him to undergo an exorcism and then to allow himself to return to death with a spotless soul. Randall, however, had other ideas and he stormed out of the house and then vanished into the night. Distressed by this turn of events, Hanlon then visited his mother Mrs Randall and discovered that the woman was not only a practising witch but that her idol was Crom Cruach, an evil pre-Christian deity from Erin, dating back thousands of years.

The stone idol of Crom, originally covered by goldleaf, once stood on the plain of Magh Slécht (the plain of adoration and prostration) in

County Cavan, surrounded by twelve lesser graven idols of bare stone. Each year on 1 November (Samhain), a third of the children of the county were sacrificed to Crom Cruach in return for fertile land, good crop yields, disease-free cattle, and good weather. The god was one of the most feared in Ireland, and there are reports of worshippers of Crom Cruach being destroyed in the very act of adoration.

The golden idol dedicated to Crom Cruach is thought to have been constructed and erected by Tigernmas, also known as the 'Lord of Death'. Little is known about this shadowy figure, but he may have been a renegade Roman legion commander who had become obsessed with the Occult.

One Samhain night, Tigernmas and three quarters of his army were lying prostrate on the ground, praying to Crom Cruach, when an unknown force destroyed them all instantly. Some accounts say lightning bolts emanating from the idol of Crom Cruach struck Tigernmas and the worshippers, leaving nothing behind but smouldering carbonised corpses. The very name Crom Cruach means 'bloody bent one' and is assumed to be a reference to the tall, crooked wraith-like entity that lurked behind the idol. This entity demanded the blood of infants, and the local population acceded to this demand by slitting the throats of a hundred babies directly over the idol.

From time immemorial the drinking of blood has been identified with the gaining of power, be it for man or a god. The Aztecs, in order to appease their graven idols, poured blood into their mouths; and the Romans were horrified when several members of the embryonic Christian sect misinterpreted the symbolic essence of Holy Communion with its ritual partaking of bread and wine. Instead, this Christian minority resorted to actual cannibalism and did indeed eat human flesh and drink human blood. In the East, the Indian Rajahs eagerly drank the blood from the severed heads of their adversaries, in order to obtain potency and vigour, and if we look at the *Book of Leviticus* in the *Old Testament*, God declares: "For the life of the flesh is in the blood; and I have given it to you upon the altar to make atonement for your souls; for it is the blood that maketh atonement by reason of the life."

Crom Cruach, the blood-drinking god of old Ireland, was chased into obscurity by St Patrick when he attacked the idol with a sledgehammer and shattered it. The shadowy parasitic thing of pure evil, that lived behind the façade of the gilded statue, fled County Cavan to an unknown destination, and some say it resorted to vampiric attacks to satisfy its insatiable lust for blood. Some occultists and witches who dealt with the most dangerous and negative form of magic continued to worship Crom Cruach, and Mrs Randall, the mother of the resurrected priest, had been one such worshipper.

After his escape, Father Randall boarded a ship at Dublin and sailed for Liverpool, not once coming on to the deck during the crossing, possibly because he had developed a heightened sensitivity to light. He may have stayed below decks by pretending to be ill, but when the ship arrived at Liverpool Docks it was already dusk, as the ship had been delayed by a violent storm. Under the cloak of darkness, Randall travelled through Liverpool to Manchester, and here he was said to have used a newly discovered talent for hypnosis, which he used to 'enslave' several women victims.

Some versions of this tale have him living right up until the 1930s, when he met a gruesome death through decapitation after being involved in a head-on car crash. Some say that Randall is buried under a false name in All Saints Cemetery, Newton Heath, Greater Manchester, and that his black marble gravestone has a cryptic symbol showing a zig-zag line enclosed in a circle with lines radiating from its perimeter – an ancient pictogram representing Crom Cruach perhaps?

A Dark and Lonely Road

There is a strange epilogue to this story. In the 1960s there was a spate of ghost sightings at All Saints Cemetery, in which a man in a long flowing black robe was seen to fly through the air over the gravestones. A woman living three hundred yards away from the cemetery on Briscoe Lane had the misfortune of seeing the ghost one night in 1967, as it looked through her bedroom window. She described the face as being of a ghastly pale colour, and that the ghoul's mouth was deep red, as if it was brimming with blood. She also described a deep and livid scar that ran right round the entity's neck; the type of scar left when they sewed the head back on to the body prior to burial perhaps?

The same apparition was seen three times during that month. It was spotted flying over the wall of a warehouse on Oldham Road at two o'clock in the morning by a nightwatchman, and a policeman also saw the same ghost hovering at the window of an old woman's house on Gaskell Street at 11pm, but the most terrifying encounter allegedly took place at midnight one night, when the black-robed phantom flew after a teenaged girl down Culcheth Lane at one o'clock in the morning.

Frances Dawson, aged just sixteen, had lost track of time at her boyfriend's house in the Dean Lane area, and suddenly realised that she should have been home an hour ago. It was pitch black outside and she pleaded with her boyfriend to escort her to her home in Culcheth, just a twelve-minute walk away. But her boyfriend had yawned and said that he wasn't feeling too well and needed to go to bed, she'd be fine on her own. Whereupon, Frances grabbed her coat, slammed the door and stormed off in a huff.

As she walked down Culcheth Lane the heavens opened and it started to pour down, and the girl quickened her pace and pulled up her coat collar against the driving rain. She was inwardly cursing her selfish boyfriend for not walking her home, when she suddenly realised that someone was walking behind her. With a sinking feeling she quickened her pace, too afraid to glance back, and with all kinds of horrific senarios playing out in her mind. The footsteps quickened their pace, keeping up with her – there was no doubt about it, she was being followed. Then they ceased abruptly, so the teenager thought she was now going to be alright and began to breathe a little more easily, although she still didn't dare look behind her and couldn't wait to reach the safety of her own home. She made herself a promise never to let herself get into this kind of situation again, if only she could get home safely this time ...

Then something swooped down on to her from the front – a grinning white-faced man in a cloak, and he hung in the air, as if he was suspended by wires. Frances screamed and instinctively ran back in the opposite direction, and as she ran along, faster than she had ever run in her life, she felt an icy cold hand snatching and tugging at her hair. She was too afraid to look up but she could see the shadow of the flying assailant all too clearly on the ground as she ran back to her boyfriend's house. It felt like a lifetime, but she eventually reached the house. As she staggered up the front steps, Frances heard a sort of sneering laughter just above her head and then silence. She hammered on her boyfriend's door and when his father answered, she charged past him without saying a word and crouched under the stairs, sobbing and trembling uncontrollably.

Although it was obvious that something had spooked her, the girl's story was not believed initially, either by her boyfriend's family, or by her own. Then the reports of other sightings started coming in – reports of a cloaked fiend who terrorised innocent female victims after dark. The local papers were full of it. Frances Dawson's parents eventually decided to take their daughter's story more seriously and accompanied her to the local police station to report the weird attacker.

The bored desk sergeant on duty eventually looked up from the crossword he was doing and asked how he could be of help. He listened to their story with ill-concealed scepticism, then, looking at his watch, he suggested that the Dawsons take their daughter home and make sure that she did not wander the streets on her own in the dark again. His rather plodding mind was unable to countenance anything remotely outside his normal sphere of activity of muggings, break-ins and petty theft. 'Irresponsible pranksters' were obviously to blame he said, by way of a parting shot, before inserting another clue into his crossword puzzle.

Another policeman who had actually witnessed the apparition himself as it levitated up to the window of a local house, was accused of being over-imaginative by the desk sergeant.

"What you need is a few early nights, lad," he said dismissively. "I know what you young 'uns are like … out every night on the booze."

However, the young constable refused to be fobbed off and kept on insisting that he had definitely seen the entity and that he was not prone to imagining things, late nights or not. In the end he was advised to 'shut up' by his superiors, or there would be unpleasant consequences.

Perhaps the ghostly assailant was just the spectre of one of the many people buried in the nearby All Saints Churchyard, or then again, perhaps it was the vampiric former priest, Father Randall, who still refused to go to his grave and was still wandering in search of blood …

OTHER TITLES BY TOM SLEMEN

HAUNTED LIVERPOOL 1	£5.99
HAUNTED LIVERPOOL 2	£5.99
HAUNTED LIVERPOOL 3	£5.99
HAUNTED LIVERPOOL 4	£5.99
HAUNTED LIVERPOOL 5	£5.99
HAUNTED LIVERPOOL 6	£5.99
HAUNTED LIVERPOOL 7	£5.99
HAUNTED LIVERPOOL 8	£5.99
HAUNTED LIVERPOOL 9	£5.99
HAUNTED LIVERPOOL 10	£5.99
HAUNTED LIVERPOOL 11	£5.99
HAUNTED LIVERPOOL 12	£5.99
HAUNTED LIVERPOOL 13	£5.99
HAUNTED LIVERPOOL 14	£5.99
STRANGE LIVERPOOL	£5.99
HAUNTED WIRRAL	£5.99
LIVERPOOL GHOST WALK	£5.99
HAUNTED CHESHIRE	£5.99
HAUNTED LIVERPOOL ANTHOLOGY	£6.99
HAUNTED LIVERPOOL double cassette and audio book read by Tom Slemen	£8.99

For a free stocklist contact visit:
www.bluecoatpress.co.uk

If you have had a paranormal encounter, or a supernatural
experience of any sort, please email Tom Slemen at:
info@bluecoatpress.co.uk